# Stories of the Saints

# Stories
# of the Saints

Retold by Siegwart Knijpenga

Floris Books

Translated by Tony Langham and Plym Peters

First published in 1993 in under the title
*Heiligen legenden* by Christofoor Publishers, Zeist
First published in English in 1997 by Floris Books
First paperback publication 2000
Reprinted 2005

British Library CIP Data available

ISBN 0-86315-325-9

Printed in Great Britain
by Bath Press, Bath

# Contents

# Foreword

Throughout the ages, the lives of the saints have left a profound influence behind them, and this has always been reflected in legends and stories which expressed the power of these lives. The stories were passed down from generation to generation, and were finally written down in the form of religious tales for adults.

The saints' lives have proved to be excellent children's stories, too. They provide a more complete and colourful picture of man than many secular stories. In selecting for this volume, we had to make a choice from an enormous range of traditional tales. Our choice was largely determined by the question of what a child between the ages of 7 and 11 is really seeking. In the stories, everything which encourages detachment from the world and reality had to be left out or transformed in a positive way. An attempt was made to do justice both to the child and to the traditional story. In describing the events of these rich lives I wrote down only what appealed to me, and what proved to have a real effect in lessons, courses, lectures and conferences.

In my choice of saints, I have kept in principle to those who have been officially canonized. And yet the question remains whether there are other inspiring examples who have been overlooked up to now. As a representative of this category, and from a sense of personal sympathy, I have also included Emma of Haarlem. She deserves to be there.

For more historical information on each saint, the reader is referred to the Appendix.

I would like to express my thanks to Bastiaan Baan, Janny Möller and Jan La Poutré. My work with them served as the inspiration for this book. In particular, I am also very grateful to Aad Meijer, who provided the biographical details and the illustrations and to Christofoor Publishers, Zeist, for producing the original illustrated edition.

Siegwart Knijpenga

# Mary

## Thus the temple became her home ...

Once upon a time, a man called Joachim and his wife Anna lived in the city of Nazareth. They had lived there for many years, and although they had a good life, they knew one great sorrow: they had no children. Yet they were good people, and followed God's commandments in everything.

They asked themselves why they had not been blessed with a child. Finally, they vowed that if God granted them a child, they would not keep it themselves. They made a promise that they would take the child to the temple in Jerusalem, so that it could be brought up there.

The time had come for Joachim to travel to Jerusalem to make his sacrifice there. He chose the best lamb from his flock as the sacrificial offering, bade farewell to his wife Anna, and started out on the journey. It was a long journey, because the great city where the temple stood was far away in the south, and it took Joachim a week to travel there.

At last, he reached the city, high up in the hills. His heart was pounding when he passed through the ancient gateway and climbed up the mountain. He saw the temple lying in front of him. There were fifteen stone steps which led him up to stand in front of the sacrificial altar.

This is where he would sacrifice the lamb which he had chosen from his flock. When it was his turn, he led the creature up towards the priest, but the latter recognized him, stepped back and said in a very severe tone of voice: "You're Joachim from Nazareth, Anna's husband. You have been married for many years, and yet God has not granted you a child. What have you done, Joachim, for your marriage to remain childless? Are you really worthy to bring a sacrifice to the altar here?"

The people who stood around were shocked. They looked at Joachim and saw that he could not think of any answer. He put the lamb down and looked at the priest, his eyes full of confusion, but the priest pointed to the steps which Joachim had just come up, and said sternly: "No one who is unworthy may bring a sacrifice here; go hence and think about your lives!"

Shaking, Joachim picked up the lamb. With downcast eyes, he turned round and left the temple, walking past rows of astonished people. He went down to the large square and left the city through the gateway known by the people as the Golden Gate. Finally, he came to the fields where shepherds were guarding their sheep, and became a servant to them.

During the daytime he worked diligently, but in the evenings he sat on his own away from the others, leaning against a rock, and thought about what he had been doing wrong all those years. Why were he and his wife unworthy? He spent many days like this, until, during one of the long, sleepless nights, he could bear it no longer. He walked into the fields, knelt down, and prayed to God to give him an answer.

Finally, towards morning, just before sunrise, the light shone around him. When he looked up, he saw an angel standing in front of him enveloped in flames, who said: "Do not be afraid, Joachim, I am the Angel of the Lord. I have known you and your wife all the days of your life. I also saw how you were sent away from the temple, and I have heard your prayer this night. I have been sent to tell you that you are not unworthy, but that you must wait until God sends the child which will now be born to you.

"The promise which you and Anna made has been accepted. The girl who will be born to you will grow up in the temple from the age of three. Her name will be Mary, and one day she will give birth to the Saviour of the world. Now get up and go back to Jerusalem. You will meet your wife under the gateway where you left the city. Go back to Nazareth with her and stay with her until your child is born."

Then the angel left him, and Joachim remained kneeling in the field, until the sun rose and the shepherds got up and prepared to go to work. Then he also got up, thanked them for allowing him to help them, and bade them farewell.

Slowly he walked back up the mountain towards the city. He was completely lost in thought because the figure of the angel who had spoken to him had been brighter than the sun which was now rising over the countryside, and he could still hear the words the angel had said, deep in his heart.

By the time Anna expected her husband back in Nazareth, the angel had also appeared to her and had given her his message. He also told her to go to Jerusalem, and so she prepared herself and followed her husband. When she reached the city and arrived at the gateway, Joachim was approaching her on another road, and they met under the shining arch of the golden gateway. They embraced and were happy. They made their sacrifice in the temple, which was now accepted by the priest, and returned to Nazareth. Not long afterwards, Anna became pregnant. They called the girl who was born to them, Mary, as the angel had said.

One day, Anna said to little Mary: "You are almost three years old, and you will soon go to Jerusalem to live there in the big temple." She took the little girl on her lap and explained to her: "Here, you can play with the children from our town, and there you will learn to bake bread for the table in the temple. You will learn to make the garments for the priests and their servants. Here you are with us, but there you will be with your teachers."

It was not long before they started out, and after a long journey they reached the temple. Up ahead, by the enormous pillars in the front porch, stood the priest beckoning to Mary. Joachim and Anna knew that the time had come for Mary to leave them, as they had promised. They kissed her and let her go. She climbed up the steps one by one without looking back, until she went into the temple, holding the priest's hand. And so the temple became the house where she lived, worked and learned everything about her people of Israel. But most of all she liked to hear the words of the Jewish prophets, who said that one day, the Messiah, the Saviour of the world, would be born from their people.

A girl cannot stay in the temple for ever. In Israel, she has to marry at the age of thirteen. The high priest called together all the unmarried men in the land. They had to bring a branch of a tree and place it in front of the altar. The man whose branch flowered would be Mary's husband.

Many men came and brought a branch with them, but none of them bore a flower. When the last man had left, the high priest looked round and saw that there was one man left in a dark corner. When the high priest asked him why he had not come forward, he said that he was just a poor old man, and surely such a beautiful young girl could not marry him.

The priest answered: "God himself will point out her husband," and commanded the man to bring his branch to the altar. And when Joseph — for that was his name — held up his branch in front of the altar, a shining white flower blossomed on the wood. Joyfully the priests exclaimed that Mary's husband had been found and that the marriage feast could soon be celebrated. And that was what happened.

# Brigid

## Have you forgotten me, Bride?

There had been a great storm at sea around the island of Iona. A small boat was bobbing up and down on the foaming, white-crested, green water, and was driven on to the coast of the island. A man got out of the boat and looked at the narrow beach, the round pebbles and the rolling hills of the countryside lying before him.

Meanwhile, a little girl had also climbed out over the edge of the boat, and when Dougal Donn — the man — looked round at her, he saw that she was kneeling down and singing a song. She was still too young to be able to talk in her own language, and therefore Dougal Donn was surprised to hear her singing in a language he didn't know. It sounded like a song of praise to the king of water, air and light.

While she was kneeling and singing, and Dougal listened to her, three men arrived. They stood in front of the child in their long white robes, and waited until she had finished her song.

Then they went to Dougal, and the middle one said: "We are Druids. I am Cathal, the Arch Druid. We saw you coming with your daughter from across the sea, from distant Ireland. We know that you are a king's son, and that you have been exiled by the king of that country and may not return. You may stay here. You will be given a piece of land to cultivate. Find yourself a wife and come and live with us. However, your daughter is no ordinary child. Let her wander over the island. The wind and the sea will be her teachers. Therefore never ask her for her secret; it will become known when the time is ripe. You yourself will be known by the name Duval. No one other than you and we will ever know that you are a king's son from Ireland."

And so Duval lived on Iona with his daughter, Brigid — or Bride, as she was known in the language of the island. She grew up there into a young woman. Duval never spoke of what the Arch Druid had told him. He knew that one day her secret would become known.

One day, when the sun was at the highest point in the heavens, Bride got up at first light. She walked outside, closed the door of the

13

hut behind her, and started to climb the hill in front of the house. When she had reached the top, the land and the sea were still covered by grey mist. After a few moments, she saw the golden glowing rim of the sun appearing above the water, and she knelt down.

She waited until the sun had appeared as a shining round disk which made everything glow around her: the blue sea, the grey rocks, the green hills and the rising mist.

And Bride sang:

> The sun is born from the night of the earth,
> It rises up
> And sends its light over the earth
> The earth warms up
> And is full of colour in its light.

Then she stood up and walked to another place on the hill where there was water, because she was thirsty. She went to a spring which is known as "the spring of youth." The water was cool and mirror-smooth underneath two rowan trees. She stepped forward underneath the overhanging branches, knelt down by the water and bent forward to drink. She saw her own face reflected in the spring, but to her astonishment, she also saw another face behind her own. It was the beautiful face of a young woman, who looked at her with a friendly expression.

She saw this face for only a moment. Then she sat up, passed her hand over her forehead, and looked around her, but there was no one there. Once again, she looked into the spring and saw only herself. She drank, stood up, and noticed, when she looked up at the two trees, that they had intertwined their crowns to form a green arch. She heard a bird sing, and saw a white blackbird flying past under the arch to the country which lay beyond.

She took courage and followed the bird. As she walked, she suddenly felt sand under her feet — hot, dry sand. The screeching of the gulls sounded further and further away, and the fragrance of the countryside was also changing. Before she knew it, she had entered a twilight world and a man she recognized as her father was standing in front of her.

"Bride, why are you so dreamy?" he said. "You wanted to get water from the spring, but what have you done with your jug? Have you forgotten it? Well, that doesn't matter, we'll find it again. What's much worse is that it hasn't rained for many weeks, and it's so dry everywhere that we're all parched. I don't have any water in my inn for my guests, and for a good innkeeper, that's very bad. I've decided to leave Bethlehem with all my donkeys and camels and go to the Mount of Olives. Apparently there's a spring there which still has water. You can stay at the inn. Come with me."

Bride followed him and came to the village of Bethlehem, where she found a lovely old inn. Dougal Donn said: "Here on this shelf there is just one bottle of water left and one barley cake. That's all I have left. You mustn't give any of it to anyone. It's just for you. You'll have to live on that until I return, and that may take three days."

People stood in the street and looked as the innkeeper Dougal Donn left Bethlehem with his animals tied one behind the other in a long line.

Bride stayed behind on her own. It was three days before she saw guests arriving. She opened the door and saw a tired old man leaning on a stick, and behind him, on a donkey, a young woman with a beautiful face. Bride saw that she was pregnant and would soon give birth to her child.

"Do you have anything to eat and drink for us?" said the man. "We have come a long way. We are also looking for somewhere to stay for the night. My name is Joseph, and this is my wife, Mary."

"I'm sorry," answered Bride, "I'm not allowed to give you anything, my father's away."

Then Mary looked at her and said: "Have you forgotten me, Bride?"

Suddenly Bride remembered the face in the spring, and she felt great joy. She opened the door and said, "Come in, Joseph and Mary. Eat some of this barley cake. Here's the bottle of water, drink as much as you like. I can't give you a place to sleep in the inn, but there's a stable behind the house with only a few animals."

Joseph and Mary were very happy with this because they were so tired. They ate and drank and then went to the stable.

Bride hurried back to the inn because she heard a rumbling in the street. There were her father's donkeys and camels coming back in a long line. Soon he had arrived at the door of the inn and pointed at the animals which were laden with full water bags. The people came running up, excited and happy. Everyone helped to unload the animals, which were fed and watered, and then stabled after their long journey. Then Dougal Donn and his daughter sat down in the inn and rested by the window.

Suddenly he sat up. "I can hear a rustling sound around the house. What can it be?"

"Yes," said Bride, "the rustling sound is approaching over the hills and it has become cooler. At last, we will have rain."

Dougal was plunged into deep thought, and then he said: "That's strange. It was predicted that when the rain comes after a long period of drought, the Christ child will be born on earth. Didn't you say that the woman in our stable was pregnant?"

They both quickly walked outside to the stable, opened the door and saw Mary seated there, surrounded by a shining light. A newborn child lay on her lap.

"Bride," said Mary, "come to Him now, the King of the elements, and rock Him on your lap tonight while I sleep."

Bride spread her cloak over her arms, Mary lay the child in her arms and Bride wrapped Him up warm in the cloak so that He wouldn't feel cold in the night. Bride rocked the child while Mary and Joseph slept. He warmed up in her cloak and suckled at her breast.

That night, the Arch Druid Cathal died on the distant island of Iona. Just before he died, he sat up and said to the brothers standing around: "I can see Bride enveloping the Lord of the Sun and the Sea in her cloak."

When he saw this he was filled with great joy, and breathed out his last breath.

Early next morning, Mary awoke. She took the child from Bride and said: "Thank you for looking after my child last night. For this service you will henceforth be known as Christ's foster mother."

When Mary had said this and had taken her child back, Bride fell into a deep sleep. She must have lain there for a long time until late in the morning. When she woke up, she found her cloak next to her, but it had changed. It was as though there were threads of gold woven through it, and it was radiant in the light shining in through the windows.

She picked up the cloak thoughtfully and left the stable. On the edge of the village she saw the footsteps of Joseph and the donkey, and followed them. On her way she gave her cloak to a sick man, who put it on and was immediately cured.

When she followed the footsteps further, she came to the desert. The sand burned the soles of her feet, and was so fine that she could no longer follow the footsteps. She walked up a hill and looked around for the road, but there was no road to be seen. As she looked round, listening for a familiar sound, she heard a blackbird sing. She saw it fly past; it was a white blackbird. It trilled its song in the clear air.

In front of her she saw two rowan trees which had intertwined their crowns to form an arch. The blackbird flew through the arch in front of her into the country that lay beyond. When she followed it she could smell the salty sea air and hear the screeching of the gulls. She bent her head and walked under the rowanberry arch.

She looked up and saw the spring next to her; in front of her lay the island of Iona and the sea. At the foot of the hill stood the cottage where she had lived. As soon as she walked down the hill the sheep and lambs came towards her and walked with her. When she arrived at the cottage she saw her father standing in the doorway. He looked older. He embraced her and said that she had been gone for a year and a day.

# Columba

## The door sprang open

### A birth foretold

Once upon a time, the chief king of Ireland left his castle early in the morning and went to a nearby spring to wash himself. On the way he thought about the queen, and felt a great sorrow. He loved her very much and they had been married for a long time, but up to now, no child had been born to them. This made him very sad.

As he was thinking about this, the king arrived at the spring. He bent forward, scooped up the water with his hands and washed himself. When he had finished he looked up and saw three figures in white robes standing before him.

The middle one started to speak, and said: "King of Ireland, you are cast down by a great sorrow because no child has yet been born from your marriage. We are angels sent by God to tell you that a son will be born to the queen within a year. He will be a powerful ruler when he becomes the chief king of Ireland. And just as your son will be king, so will your grandchildren and great grandchildren. And their children and grandchildren will also be mighty rulers. Finally, after hundreds of years, a man will be born from your lineage who will change Ireland and Scotland. He will love God as no other, and he will carry out God's will on earth, so that God will love him too. He will be called Columba. He will be the twelfth descendant in your lineage. For his sake you will be blessed with the birth of your son."

The child was born within a year, just as the three angels had foretold. He became a mighty ruler, and centuries later, Columba was born from his lineage.

## The precious cloak

Shortly before Columba's birth, his mother Ethne had a dream. An angel stood by her and brought her a precious cloak which glowed in many colours. He gave her this cloak and she took it into her hands. She saw that it was woven from the colours of many flowers.

While she was looking at this and her heart trembled with joy for its beauty, the angel bent towards her and took the cloak from her again. He raised it up and spread it out above her to its full width.

Ethne was sad, and said to the angel: "Why are you taking it away when you have only just given it to me?"

The angel answered: "This cloak is for someone so light and strong that you can no longer keep it." As he spoke these words, she saw that the cloak moved away from her and rose up to heaven, becoming larger and larger. It spread itself out above the fields, the woods, the mountains and finally, above the whole country where she lived.

Ethne was still full of the beauty of the colourful cloak, which now surrounded her on every side, and the angel said to her: "Do not be sad, but rejoice: you will bear a son who will be a prophet and who will show countless people the way to heaven. His name will be Columba."

## The wolf and the dove

When the child was born, his father took him into his arms and said: "This is a strong child. We shall call him Crimthan, which means wolf."

However, the mother had heard from the angel that he would be called Columba, which means dove. And so he had these two names. Later he knew that he had first been named Crimthan, but he preferred to use the name Columba, and it is by that name that he became known to the world.

## The book

When he grew up he wanted to become God's servant, and at an early age he left his mother to live with the monks. After that, he wandered through Ireland, through fields and woods, by the seashore and across the mountains. From the mountains he could see the whole country. He saw that it became dark when there was storm and rain, and he saw the splendid glowing colours when the sun broke through and the black clouds were driven away by the light. Then the storm would be still and the people would come outside again. Columba often sat in his little room and wrote page after page in small black letters and large colourful capital letters. This is how he learned to write, from the books of the monks.

When he was forty years old, he went to visit the monastery of his former teacher, Ninian, who had been given a beautiful book. Columba went to his writing table every evening to copy the stories from this book, and made his own book. However, when he had finished, it was discovered and he was brought before the abbot of the monastery, who was angry because Columba had not asked him for permission. He said to him: "The book you wrote is my book, because you copied it from my book. When you leave, you'll have to leave it here."

Columba answered: "You have your book. This is not changed in any way because I have copied it. I would like my people to read it, and therefore I do not wish to leave it behind here."

The abbot and Columba could not agree, and when their dispute was submitted to the king, he said that the abbot was right. Columba was so furious that in his anger, he took the book, left Ninian's house, and called on the armies of his family and friends.

He waged war against the king, and Columba's warriors defeated the king's soldiers, who fled. Three thousand people were killed in the battle.

## To Iona

Columba's men celebrated the victory with a great feast. Columba also celebrated, but in the following days he constantly looked at the book and thought about the battle and the many people who had died. That night when he wanted to sleep, he also thought of these things and could not sleep. He thought: was it right that so many people had to die for the sake of a book? Finally, he became very sad, and started to feel that he should no longer live in the land where he had brought such bad luck to so many people. And so he decided to leave Ireland and to go where the sea and the wind would show him a place to live.

He found twelve monks who were willing to go with him, and prepared a boat with them. However, he broke off the rudder before their eyes and threw it on to land. He also removed the sail from the mast. Then they went aboard and allowed the currents of the sea to guide the rudderless boat.

They drifted north a long way until they could no longer see Ireland. At last, they caught sight of a small green island. The boat drifted towards it and landed on a beach in a small bay with beautiful round pebbles. It was the same place where Dougal Donn and the little Bride had landed a hundred years earlier. Columba also met the Druids in their long white cloaks here, and they were glad that he had come to join them on the island.

Columba thanked the Druids for their hospitality. He went inland, and in the following years he built houses, made many journeys and finally lived on this small island for thirty years with his monks. In those days it was called Hy. It is said that Columba gave it the name Iona.

## Barley

A great deal of wood was needed to build the houses. Columba sent his monks to a farmer who lived on the island to ask for wooden posts and beams. The monks returned, bringing what Columba had asked for, but they said: "The farmer gave us the wood, but he does think that we asked for rather a lot. He hopes that he will have enough left for himself."

"In that case, we must give him something in return," answered Columba. He took three measures of barley from his supplies, blessed them and gave them to the monks, with orders for the farmer to sow this barley. By the following month it would have grown and be ripe in the field.

When the monks went to the farmer, he did not believe them. No one who sows in July can have ripe barley by August. However, he did what he had been asked, and Columba's prediction proved to be correct.

A month later the full ears of golden-yellow barley were ripe in the field. The farmer harvested and threshed the crop and had plenty to eat all winter long; he was also able to share his grain with others, and had enough left over for sowing the next crop.

## The doors sprang open

Actually, the island of Iona belonged to the Scottish king, Brude, and Columba decided to visit this ruler. With several other monks, he crossed over to Scotland and sailed up the river to the end of the large lake called Loch Ness. The royal palace lay hidden in the mountains above the landing place. They moored their boat and climbed up the rocky path to the fortress.

The land was rocky and bare. A chill wind blew around the mountain walls, and the mist made it difficult to find the way. However, Columba walked ahead, undeterred by anything. Just in front of them, they glimpsed a guard who quickly walked away, "He is announcing our arrival," said Columba.

When they arrived at the lofty fortress, the great doorway was closed. The monks knocked and called out, but nobody answered or opened the door. King Brude had ordered that it should be barred to strangers and be kept locked. However, Columba started singing in a powerful voice:

> My heart trembles with joy
> because I wish to sing for you, O king.

Then he made the sign of the Cross and placed his hands on the door. At that moment the locks broke, and the heavy wooden doors gave way on both sides, swinging back so that the monks could enter the fortress.

The king was struck with terror. Was this stranger mightier than he, though he had ordered the doors to be shut? No one had ever been able to break the locks. He hastened down the stairway and hurried towards them, bowing deeply before Columba, to welcome him.

Columba honoured him as a king, and they pledged friendship to each other. King Brude agreed that the monks could live on Iona, and granted them the island as their home.

## Into the wind

The Arch Druid in Brude's kingdom, Broichan, also lived in the fortress. He had seen how the doorway had sprung open for Columba, and was jealous of the latter's power. Who was this stranger who could simply enter their fortress just like that? He decided to show Columba that he had even greater magical powers himself.

"When are you thinking of leaving?" he asked.

Columba answered, "We will set sail in three days' time."

"We'll see about that," Broichan answered threateningly. "A powerful wind will prevent you from sailing on the lake."

Columba said: "The highest God rules over you and me and over the wind. It's in His hands whether we will sail or not."

Broichan laughed mockingly and turned away.

Three days later the monks left the fortress and went down the path to Loch Ness, followed by the Druids and a large crowd. When they arrived at the lake, a strong wind was blowing straight towards the mooring place, and a threatening black cloud was building up over them. The boat rocked violently on the waves, whipped up by the fierce gusts of wind.

The crowd huddled on the banks and the monks stood around Columba, who ordered them to get into the boat and hoist the sails. They looked at him fearfully, but in a strong voice he commanded them to obey. And so they hoisted the sails, and at a sign from Columba the boat sailed out into the wind under its own power. After a few moments the cloud broke up, the wind dropped and turned, and the men had the wind behind them to reach the sea and sail to Iona.

## The crane

Once Columba called one of his monks to him and said: "In three days' time you must go to the beach in the west. A guest will arrive there on the ninth hour of the day. This guest is a poor crane who has flown here from Northern Ireland. It has been so buffeted by the wind that it will arrive at the beach completely exhausted. Pick it up and take it to the people in the house nearby. They will look after it. There is no need for them to be afraid that it will fall ill or never leave, for after three days it will have regained its strength and will fly back to Ireland."

This is what happened. Exhausted from the flight through the storm, the bird fell to the beach completely starved. The monks found it and took it in their arms to a house where a fisherman lived. He, his wife and his children were pleased to look after it. They made a nest, fed it and let it rest. They did this for three days.

Then the wind dropped, the sea was smooth and the sun appeared in a cloudless sky. At that moment the crane spread its wings and flew up. For a minute it hovered above the house of the fisherman and his family, who had looked after it, to thank them and bid them farewell. Then it turned to the south and flew directly and quickly back to Ireland.

## The sorrowing white mare

Columba had grown old. He had lived on Iona for thirty years and was tired of all the work he had done. He had already said to his monks: "I will not be with you much longer, but do not feel sad about me. I see lots of light, and that is where I will go."

Finally, one Saturday he was walking to the grain shed with Diormit, a monk who was supporting him. He saw the grain which had been harvested, and said to Diormit: "You will have enough grain for a while. You don't have to worry."

Then he sat down on a rock to rest and said: "Today is Saturday, the day which is also called the Sabbath, and which is really a day of rest. For me, Diormit, this is a very special day of rest, because I can now take a rest from my whole life. I am entrusting you with this secret which you may not pass on yet: you should know that tonight at the beginning of Sunday morning, I will leave you and return to the great light where angels are calling to me to come."

Diormit was shocked, and wept for his abbot, who was so dear to him.

When he looked up, he saw the white mare which always carried the milk from the meadow to the house, coming towards them on the path. The horse stopped by Columba, placed its head in his lap, and big tears rolled from its eyes. Diormit wanted to chase away the white mare, but Columba said: "Don't you see that this creature knows that I am going to die? That's why it is weeping. Let it be, it is bidding me farewell."

So the animals and people bade farewell to Columba. On the Sunday morning following the Saturday, a great light appeared above the water on the coast of the island. It was not the sun, for this would not rise until much later. It was the Archangel Michael himself who stood there. He sang a song for Columba and took him with him to his realm.

# Francis of Assisi

## Until the roses bloom again

### Rich, and born on straw

At the time that Francis was about to be born, his father, Pietro Bernadone, was travelling. He was trading large rolls of woven material in France; silk, linen, cotton and wool, all in the warm colours which people liked to use for making their clothes for feast days.

His wife Pica had stayed behind in the stately merchant's house in Assisi; she was expecting a child. But the days passed and she became restless. She didn't understand why it was taking so long. Everything was prepared in the large, sunny nursery.

However, one day Pica heard someone knocking at the front door. An old man stood before her. His wrinkled face and bright blue eyes were surrounded by grey hair. He did not ask for money or bread, but said to her: "A child wishes to be born to you, but it does not wish to come to you in wealth. It wants to have a cradle in the straw."

When Pica heard these words and felt the eyes of the old man resting on her, she knew in her heart that he was speaking the truth. She hurried to have straw brought down to a room at the bottom of the house, and that very day her son was born.

She gave him the name Giovanni, which means John. However, his father named him after the French with whom he had traded. And therefore he was known to the people as Francesco, or as we now call him, Francis.

He made everyone who saw him happy, for he liked to play, he liked to learn, he loved everyone and he knew how to have a good time.

## Lady Poverty

Once he held a party with his many friends. They all gathered together in their bright, colourful clothes, eating, drinking and playing, and when evening fell they walked through the streets and squares of Assisi in the dark, singing merrily.

A few people approached from the other direction, and the partying band walked in single file on one side of the street. Francis lagged behind. The narrow street was dimly lit; there was little light from above, and suddenly Francis noticed that an unusual woman was passing on the opposite side of the street. She was more beautiful than any woman he had every seen, but she wore only a coarse brown robe down to her feet, and nothing else. She didn't speak a word, and passed by him silently as he looked. He didn't speak either. His heart asked: "Who are you?" and he received the answer: "This, Francis, is Lady Poverty."

When she disappeared into the dusk, Francis leant against the wall of the house where he was standing and followed her with his gaze. Not for long, however, because his friends had noticed he was missing and had come back.

"You're dreaming, you look as though you've seen a beautiful woman," they called to him.

"Yes, I have," he murmured, and blushing, he added: "A woman who is more beautiful than any other; I have met my bride, the most beautiful woman on earth."

His friends were astonished, but they were not the only ones. His parents — and everyone else in Assisi — were surprised by what happened. Francis bade farewell to his father's wealth and devoted his life to Lady Poverty. He gave everything he owned back to his father, or gave it away until he did not own anything any more. From that day a new life started for him.

## The birds

Francis had been on the road for a long time. When evening fell, his path led through a meadow. Suddenly he heard birds singing and he looked up. Thrushes and blackbirds were singing in the treetops, the odd woodpecker hopped along the trunk, giving its short, bright call; wrens and goldcrests were perched in the bushes, and larks were swooping up and down over the meadow, all singing and chirping.

Francis stood still, and then walked into the middle of the meadow.

He greeted all the birds around him and beckoned to them with his hand. When they saw him, they stopped singing, fluttered towards him and flew down to the meadow all around him, until the whole meadow was full of birds. It was as though they knew that Francis wished to speak to them, and this is what happened.

As soon as they all fell silent and raised their little heads to him, he said: "Dear birds, dear brothers and sisters, how rich you are, how much the Creator has given you. We humans have a long road to travel every day. You simply spread your wings and you can fly anywhere very quickly. You can live in the air, and that is a great gift. Furthermore, you have been given a beautiful cloak of feathers which may be brighter for some of you than for others, but is beautiful for all of you. And then you have all been given such wonderful voices. People often have to try very hard to learn to sing, but you are all able to sing without having to learn.

"When I heard you singing as I walked past, I heard the most beautiful thing; I heard you sing a song of thanks to the Creator for everything you have received. Sing this song of thanks always, as well as you can!"

When Francis had finished speaking, the birds started flapping and beating their wings. They stretched out their little heads and started to sing again, this time even more loudly and jubilantly than before. Francis heard them and realized that the birds had understood him. He raised his right hand and made the sign of the Cross over them. Then he gestured to them that they could fly away. They did so — some flew where the sun was rising, others where the sun was setting. The third group went where the sun is highest in the heavens, and the last group went where the sun never shines.

They continued to sing, and as they sang they moved from the place where their brother Francis had spoken to them in the four directions of the Cross — to the east and west, to the north and south — so that their song of thanks would sound throughout the land.

## The wolf of Gubbio

The people in the town of Gubbio were having a bad time. An enormous wolf, which did not respect anyone or anything, lived near the town. It not only devoured chickens, sheep and cattle, but when it was ravenously hungry, it even attacked people.

When Francis came to the town and the inhabitants told him about this, he felt pity for them and decided to go to the wolf. The people of Gubbio begged him to remain within the walls, for the wolf had killed so many people already; others wanted to give him a sword and spear to take with him, but the holy man said:

> Stronger than your spear and sword
> Is Jesus Christ, my Lord.

And he left the town, unarmed, with one of his monks, passing through the gateway, which the guard immediately shut behind him. The people climbed on to the town wall because they all wanted to see what would happen. They were worried for Francis's life because they loved him very much.

He and the other monk walked straight towards the wolf's lair, and the wolf ran out towards them, its mouth wide open, ready to tear them to pieces. As the wolf leaped towards them, Francis stood still and made the sign of the Cross from top to bottom and from left to right. Then something happened that no one had dared to hope for. The savage beast stood still, closed its mouth and bent its cruel head down. It was still growling, but when Francis started to speak it calmed down and seemed to listen to him. Finally, it lay down with its ears pricked up.

"Brother wolf," said the holy man, "you are doing a great deal of harm in this area. You are killing not only chickens, sheep and cattle, but you also dare to attack people. Everyone is afraid of you, and in addition, they hate you because you do so much harm. Therefore you should be punished like a thief and a robber; you deserve to be killed. This is what the people think who you see standing there on the wall.

However, I do not come to punish you, but I want there to be peace between you and the inhabitants of the town. Brother wolf, I suggest that from now on you do not kill anyone any more, and that the people stop hunting you with their dogs."

The wolf nodded and moved its tail to show that it agreed to this, and then Francis continued: "Of course, I know very well, brother wolf, that you only do all that because you're always so hungry. I understand that, and therefore I suggest that in future the people of this town will make sure that your hunger is satisfied. When this has been agreed with the people, will you stop hurting them? Will you promise?"

The wolf nodded vehemently as a sign that it agreed to this.

The holy man then went on: "Brother wolf, I give you my hand as a sign of this agreement and to show that I trust that we can keep it."

The wolf raised its hairy right paw and placed it as carefully as it could in Francis's narrow hand.

Then Francis concluded, as he let go of the wolf's paw and stood next to him to look towards the town: "Brother wolf, come with us now. If you follow me and my friend, everything will be alright. I give you my word."

And so the two monks and the mighty wolf entered the town. The people fell silent in amazement and flocked to the large square in the middle of Gubbio, where the wolf sat down and Francis spoke to the crowd. He told them what had happened, and that the wolf had promised henceforth not to harm anyone. He asked the inhabitants to give the wolf enough to eat, and to make sure that their dogs would not chase it any more.

The people agreed to this, and from that day on, the wolf which had been feared, now became a friendly wolf which went from house to house and was given something to eat at every door until it had eaten its fill. And it was not only the people who kept their word; the dogs no longer barked or growled at it either.

For two years the wolf lived with the people of Gubbio in this way. Never again was it a thief or a robber, but it took and ate what the people gave it. However, it was no longer a young wolf. It had lived a long life, and if it hadn't been grey already, it would certainly have gone grey now. The people of the town saw that it was growing old and tired, and were not surprised when one day it did not come to the town to walk past the houses. It died quietly in its lair in the woods.

When it no longer came to them, the people rather missed it, and they did not forget it. Thus it was that in winter when the fire was burning in the hearth in the evening, children would often say: "Grandmother, can you tell us the story of the wolf of Gubbio this evening?"

## Francis and Clare

Clare was a noblewoman. She was called Donna Clara by the many people who knew and admired her. The Offreducio family, of which she was a member, lived in a grand house which stood on the mountainside above the town of Assisi. It looked out over the town and the surrounding rolling countryside.

Below Assisi there was a chapel in a valley between the gentle hills, which was so small that there was room for only a few people. It was called Portiuncula. Clare knew that there was a man staying in this Portiuncula who had once been the son of a rich merchant, but who did not want to own anything and had therefore given everything away to live with the strength of poverty. More and more people had joined him to live as he did.

She often sat by the window and looked down at the place where this man lived, and she felt that she wanted to live like he did. But she didn't know how. After all, she was the rich and important noblewoman of Offreducio. Couldn't she leave her family and wealth behind her as he had done, for the sake of holy poverty? Would she have the courage to leave her noble house to live in a hut in the woods?

One day she met Francis. He was standing in the square in the middle of the town and spoke to the people. His words touched her so profoundly that she decided to leave her parents' home that very night.

In the evening, as soon as darkness fell, a trusted servant opened the door for her, and Donna Clara went down, passing the town and beyond to the woods where the small Portiuncula chapel stood. That evening she also left all her possessions behind her, and became a sister of the brothers who followed Francis.

"You can be born brother and sister and look like one another externally," Francis had said. "You can also find one another as brother and sister and look like each other internally."

Clare realized that no one was as close to her as Francis, and she was happy to call herself his sister.

On one occasion they had both been away for a long time to comfort and look after the sick, and they returned home very late. They were hungry and thirsty, and so they knocked at the door of a dwelling to ask for some bread and water. As they ate and drank, they heard what the people thought of them; how they were mocked and laughed at behind their backs. They whispered, "We have to work hard to earn this bread, and those two who are eating it are having a good time together."

Francis continued on his way, Clare walking in front of him. "Did you hear what the people think of us?" he asked after a while.

Clare nodded, but could not answer. She knew what was going to happen, and it filled her with sorrow.

"Clare, you must go to your sisters and I will go to my brothers. We will not see each other for a while," said Francis.

Then Clare turned round in the middle of the road and asked him: "For how long, brother Francis?"

He looked round and saw the bare trees and the bushes and hedges which were white and stiff with rime, because it was winter. And he answered: "Not until the roses bloom again."

The tears came to Clare's eyes because she knew that roses do not bloom until summer. But when she looked up, she saw to her surprise that there were red roses blooming on the snowy white hedges in such large numbers that she could not count them.

She was filled with great joy, ran towards the hedges and picked an armful of roses. She placed them in Francis's hands, and they understood that He who makes roses bloom in winter liked to see them working together for the sick and the poor.

## Brother Fire

Francis sat in the doorway of his hut in semi-darkness, looking out. He could hardly see the things around him because his eyes were becoming weak. The doctor had said that he would not be able to use them much longer. He realized that he had little time left to see and understand everything around him.

He felt that the sun was his brother, and the moon and the stars his sisters, for they gave him light, which makes all things visible. The wind had brought a freshness and the cloud a welcome shade and rain. They too, were brothers and sisters, as were the springs of water and the whole earth itself. During this time, Francis wrote a song about them which he would be able to sing, even when his eyes could no longer see them.

He waited for the doctor who wanted to try and help him. The doctor wanted to brand his temples next to his eyes with a glowing iron bar. Perhaps this would cure him.

Francis was not afraid of fire, but he knew that glowing iron is very painful. However, he thought: "Glowing fire, you too are my brother."

When the doctor arrived and put the hot iron to his head, he said: "Fire, be a mild brother to me. Help me, and extinguish your terrible heat so that I can bear the pain." When the doctor touched his temples, Francis felt the force of the fire, but he did not feel any pain. He thanked the fire for not adding to his suffering with its heat.

## Brother Death

Finally, the day came when Francis's life reached fulfilment. Once again he was sitting in the door of his hut, and he looked up. At that moment a mighty cloud approached and slid in front of the sun. The dark cloud stood in the sky, but the edges burned with a fiery golden glow. Rays of light shone in every direction across the sky.

Francis felt the shadow which the clouds cast over him, and the coolness which it brought, and he said softly and thoughtfully: "You bring me darkness, brother cloud, and coolness, but brother sun lives behind your darkness. In this way you remind me of my brother death. For anyone who is led through his dark gate reaches true light; therefore you are welcome too, my brother death."

Thus Francis departed from all those he had called his brothers and sisters, and they all mourned him. But they also sang the song that he had written and which ended by speaking of death as his brother. When they sang the words of this song, they remembered how Francis had sung it himself, and they were joyful, as in the days when he was still in their midst.

# Giles

## Let us ask the earth

Giles, the son of the king of Greece, said to his parents one day: "Mother and father, let me go. I want to travel to distant lands, and I want to wander until I find a place where no man has yet set foot. Mother, give me food to take with me, and father, give me your blessing."

His mother gave him some food and drink, and his father said, "Go and seek this place, and when you have found it, stay as long as you can. May God's blessing be on you!"

And so Giles went on his way. He travelled to the land where the sun sets. He journeyed further and further west until he came to the country of France. Finally, he entered a large wood. There was no path which led him into the wood. He walked over hills and along abysses, and found the way through the dense, dark wilderness.

When he had walked a long way, he saw a light shining between the tree trunks. He walked towards it, and suddenly found himself standing in a small clearing in the woods. On the other side of this clearing, there was a rock with a cave in it, and next to the cave there was the source of a spring. A lot of green grass grew by the water, which flowed away in a small stream, and there were countless colourful flowers. Giles took a few paces forward and stood in the full sunlight. Then he walked across the meadow to the cave, which was large enough to live in. He drank from the spring and decided to stay.

He had finished the food and drink he had brought with him. He looked around and discovered berries and roots to eat in the woods, and when the time came that there was no more fruit and roots, he sat in front of his cave thinking of how he could find food. Suddenly a hind sprang from the shrubs. Her light brown skin shone in the sunlight of the meadow beyond the shadow of the woods. She approached Giles and indicated that he could drink her milk, and he was pleased to do so.

From then on, she came to him every morning and every evening, so that he was never thirsty again. She knew the way to him. Ever since he had lived there, thorns with large red roses had appeared all around the open meadow in the woods, and finally grew to form a thick hedge which surrounded the whole place. However, the hind came in through a narrow opening, and left by the same opening.

One day, the huntsmen of the king of that country had penetrated into the wood so far that they had come to the place where Giles lived. There the hind happened to cross their path. The huntsmen had never seen such a splendid animal and wanted to hunt her. They unleashed the dogs and spurred on their horses. Their horns sounded through the whole woods, and they hunted the hind until evening fell.

When she was almost surrounded, she bent forward and wriggled through the opening in the rose hedge and lay down before Giles, completely exhausted. The dogs barked furiously. They howled and bayed because they could not get in through the hedge. But evening fell and the huntsmen went home with their dogs.

The next evening they started hunting again. The huntsmen followed her until the evening and saw how the hind suddenly disappeared, and the dogs ran to that place, furiously turning this way and that because they could not find a way through the hedge of thorns, and they stood there astonished.

The king himself heard about it and rode up, full of curiosity. This time he told his men to take their swords and hack a path through the thorns. As they did so, one of the huntsmen shot an arrow over the hedge to try and hit the hind. However, it hit Giles, and he was badly wounded.

When the men had hacked a path through the hedge, the king passed in through the roses and saw Giles sitting in front of his cave with the hind at his feet. He greeted him cordially and asked how he came to be there and what he was doing. When Giles had told him everything, the king asked him who had wounded him with the arrow, and when he heard that it had been one of his own huntsmen he felt guilty and wanted to take him with him and nurse him. However, Giles said: "Lord where would you take me? This is the best place in your whole kingdom, protected by a hedge of roses in a large cave in the middle of your woods and yet in direct sunlight. Only here can I be cured, Lord."

The king asked: "Shall I send a doctor to see you?"

Giles declined: "My doctor is always with me in this place. He will cure me." That happened just as Giles had said.

The king often visited the quiet place in the woods and was always happy and content when he had been there. Even when he felt sick, he went and felt better. After him, many others also came to visit Giles, and everyone who came was helped or cured of their sickness or distress.

## The white lilies

One day, a rich young man came to visit Giles. He leapt down from his horse and walked in by the path through the hedge. Without greeting Giles, he began speaking. "Hermit, they say that you know a great deal. The people maintain that your eyes can see things that are invisible to others. Tell me, is it true that it is the angels who bring children to earth? Jesus was also supposedly brought to Mary by an angel. That is what the people say. Hermit, I can't believe it."

Giles asked: "My good man, how do you recognize angels?"

The man cried: "How can I know that, if I can't see them?"

Giles said: "An angel has a robe that is so pure and white that it could never belong to a human. Let us ask the earth, she is older and wiser than we are."

On a stretch of sand next to the cave he wrote with his finger: "What are the angels like who bring the children down to earth?"

And three lilies sprang up from the sand. They opened their white petals and shone in the sun.

"This is how light the robes of the angels are," said Giles, pointing to the lilies, "and lighter than all others is the angel that brought Jesus to Mary."

# Benedict

## Why is the last stone so heavy?

### The spring

Benedict lived with his fellow monks in a hilly region on the banks of the river. The river gave them the water they needed to live. Benedict, whose hut was close to the bank, had only to walk down the hill to fetch some water. A number of the monks had built their huts high up on the rock and they had to go down a long steep path to reach the river. Then they had to carry the water back up the narrow rocky path in leather water bags. This was such a heavy task, that they constantly complained to Benedict to allow them to build their hut down by the bank as well. But Benedict answered that some monks had to live high up the mountain. However, he promised to think about it and see if he could do anything about it.

One evening after sunset, he left his hut and climbed up the path which led to where the monks lived. However, it was a steep climb, and when Benedict looked from the edge at the top, he saw the river glistening down below in the moonlight. Then he felt pity for the monks. He went to a large rock which lay between their huts and knelt in front of it. He touched the rock and said:

> May our thirsty mouths receive
> water from this hard ground
> from you who succours all life,
> the Lord of heaven and earth.

Then he stood up and placed three white pebbles on the rock and went back down the path to his hut.

The following morning the monks again knocked at his door. They were coming from the river carrying their heavy bags. Once again they asked him if they could not come to live further down.

"No," said Benedict, "you are my brothers in the mountains. But

41

go up and see if you can find three pebbles. Then take a staff and strike it in that place and God will give you water."

Joyfully the monks climbed back up and found the pebbles. They all gathered around the place and looked expectantly as the oldest amongst them raised his staff and struck the rock. Behold, clear cool water flowed out. It flowed down over the side of the rock, by the huts and over the edge of the mountain. It became a spring from which water always flowed, and where everyone could quench their thirst.

## The sickle

Near Benedict's hut there was a meadow full of flowers, and in the middle of this meadow there was a deep pond. Some thorny thistles grew amongst the grass and the flowers, and Benedict had asked a young monk to remove these weeds with a sickle. Thistles are tough, and the monk was not always able to remove them at one stroke. The thorns pricked him, and he struck at the thistles more and more furiously to cut down the tough stalks. Once he swung the sickle so violently that the blade suddenly flew off the wooden handle in a great arc to fall into the middle of the pond.

The monk could only look. He was left holding the handle, feeling crestfallen and not knowing what to do. Sorrowfully he sat down on the grass.

Benedict saw him sitting there, and because he understood what had happened, he went up to him, asked him for the handle, and then put it into the pond himself. Then he said:

> Iron that shone in the sunlight,
> and sank to the depths with your fury,
> return at my command,
> to the wood where you belong.

When Benedict raised the handle up from the water the blade had leaped back into the handle and shone in the light as it had done before. Then the monk cut down thistle after thistle with strong sure strokes, until the whole meadow was cleared.

## *The child*

There was a child who went to fetch water on the river bank with a scoop. When he bent down and plunged the scoop into the fast flowing river, the current was so strong that the child slipped and fell in. He was quickly dragged along by the current, away from the safe bank and into the middle of the river.

Benedict, who was in his hut, saw what happened through the window. He called to Brother Maurus and commanded him to save the child from the river.

"Father, give me your blessing, so that the strong current does not drag me along," called Maurus.

And Benedict placed his hand on his head and said:

> On your way
> through water or land,
> receive God's blessing
> from my hand.

Maurus hurried through the door, through the garden and across the rocky path to the river. Without hesitating, he went straight to the place where the child had been swept away. He walked across the water as though it was firm land, reached the child, pulled him from the water and brought him back to the bank.

Returning full of astonishment, Maurus told Benedict what had happened, but Benedict said: "The fact that the water bore you up is not thanks to me, but because you did what was necessary for the child."

## *The raven and the poisoned bread*

Every morning and every evening, a raven came to Benedict's window and waited until the holy man stretched out his hand with some bread.

One day, Benedict's enemy Florentinus sent him a poisoned loaf. When Benedict saw it, he put it aside until the evening when the raven came to his window. He opened the window put out the bread ready, and said: "Dear raven, take this bread and take it to a place where no one will ever find it. But take care that you do not eat any of it yourself."

The raven opened its beak wide and wanted to take hold of the loaf, but could not. Then it started to flap its wings, tripped around the loaf and cawed loudly, as if to say it could not take the bread.

However Benedict said:

> Take it away and then come back to me.
> Do this in the name of Our Lord.
> He knows the food of good and evil.
> He will take care of you, have courage.

The raven picked up the bread carefully, flew off and took it to a hidden place. Then it returned to Benedict's window and ate from his hand as it always had.

## The devil on the rock

A large house was built where many of the monks were to live together. Stone after stone was lifted up, given to the bricklayer and put into place. There was one opening left, and when the last stone was put into place, the wall would be finished and the house would be ready.

This stone, which is known as the keystone, was ready, and one of the brothers picked it up with both hands, tried to lift it to give to the bricklayer, but no matter what he did the monk was unable to lift it from the ground. The other monks came and joined him and pulled with all their might, but they could not move it. When they looked up they saw Benedict standing there. "It's the last stone. Why is it so heavy?"

Benedict said: "Now you will learn who it is who holds the key stone." He stepped forward and said:

> Devil in the stone.
> Go! And do not return!

When he had said these words, they heard a scream which was lost in the distance in a gust of wind.

At a sign from Benedict the monks then picked up the stone, and it was placed in the wall so that the house was finished and the work was done.

## The road to heaven

The night before Benedict died, two monks had the same dream. They saw a path leading from Benedict's house right up to the gate of heaven. The path was strewn with colourful carpets, and burning candles stood on either side.

A friendly old man stood at the foot of the path and asked: "Do you know who will take this path?"

They both said that they did not know, and the old man answered: "It is Benedict who will take this path, when he has finished his task on earth."

# Jerome

## Brothers, the lion wishes to stay with us

Jerome was a famous man. Everyone knew him because he travelled throughout the world. He would travel for months on end, but in between his journeys he would sit at his table day after day writing his thick books in Greek, Latin and Hebrew. He built a large monastery with many rooms, together with his fellow monks, and with his own hands he would help with the building and with whatever needed doing. In this house he had a special friend, and this story is about that friend.

One day, this friend came to the doorway of the big courtyard around which all the monks' rooms were built. As the doorway was half open, he walked in and sat down in the middle of the courtyard next to the fountain there and swung his tail about. With his yellowish green eyes and powerful head, he looked at the windows and finally straight into the face of one of the monks who was looking out.

This monk called out excitedly: "A lion, brothers! There's a lion in the courtyard. Quickly, go and hide." The monks ran through the corridors and shut themselves into their rooms peering anxiously through the windows into the courtyard to see what would happen next.

But Jerome had also seen the lion. He had seen more than the monk who had raised the alarm. In fact, he had noticed that the lion was dragging one of its feet and had come in lame. He stood up and told the monks that this lion had not come to kill or rob them, but because it needed help. And so he walked outside and sat down next to the creature. Carefully he took the painful paw into his hand, and found that a large thorn was stuck in it. The lion quietly let him examine it, and Jerome carefully pulled out the thorn. Then he treated the wound, bandaged it up and finally gave the creature something to eat.

A few days later the lion had recovered, but to everyone's surprise, it remained lying in the courtyard. It had food brought to it and didn't hurt anyone. It was particularly attached to Jerome, who had helped him, and looked at him as if to say, "I belong with you, give me something to do."

"Brothers," Jerome said, "the lion wishes to stay with us, and because he is now one of us, he will also have to work. From now on he will accompany the donkey that brings wood from the forest, to protect it and make sure it doesn't run away." The lion was informed of this task and from the day his paw was cured he went into the forest with the donkey every morning and came back with it every evening. Then they would both be fed, and everyone was happy.

However, one day the lion was very was tired, and while the donkey was waiting for the wood to be fetched from the forest, its protector put his head on his front paws and fell asleep. He slept so soundly that he did not notice a group of merchants passing by with camels. The merchants saw the donkey standing alone, took hold of the reins and pulled it away with them. No matter how it pulled and stretched its legs and brayed loudly, the merchants would not let go, and the lion did not notice anything as he was sleeping so soundly.

But later that afternoon he did wake up. He yawned, stretched, looked around and was horrified to see that the donkey was gone. The lion jumped up, ran round roaring loudly, and looked behind every hill and in every bush, but could not find his friend anywhere. It was dreadful. He came back to the door of the monastery much later than usual, his head hanging in shame.

That evening, when the monks saw him walking up like this, they kept the door shut. They thought that at last he had done what any other lion would have done — he had eaten the donkey. "You're not having anything this evening," they cried. "Go and find the remains of the donkey, that'll be enough for you."

The lion was very sad. He did not walk away, but lay down and waited patiently until the monks finally opened the door for him and let him in, shaking their heads. He lay down in the centre of the courtyard that evening and the next day and waited to be given a new job to do.

Jerome, who saw this, said: "Dear lion, whether or not you ate the donkey, you will have to do something. You'll have to take over the donkey's task."

And so the lion walked through the doorway to the forest with the monks every morning, waited until they had fetched the wood and had it loaded up, and then carried it back home for them. Then he was fed in the courtyard.

However, one day he felt restless. After dinner he did not roll over on to his side to go to sleep, but paced up and down by the doorway for so long that one of the monks opened the door. Then he walked into the field and looked around.

In the distance he saw a group of merchants approaching with their camels. They were heavily laden with casks full of precious oil. In front of them was a donkey. This is easier for camels, as a donkey can find its way better than they can.

Suddenly the lion recognized his friend, the donkey. He jumped up and leapt towards the procession. He thumped his tail wildly and roared so loudly that the whole earth shook.

At first, the merchants were rigid with terror. Then they let go of the reins of their animals and fled into the forest as quickly as they could. However, the lion chased all the animals, and drove them to the courtyard of the monastery. Then the lion walked to the donkey, stood next to it and licked it, and the donkey brayed with joy at finding its old friend.

The monks heard this, and one by one they looked curiously through the window. Then they went to Jerome to ask him what it meant.

"It means," said Jerome, "that in a few moments we will have some guests at the door. Prepare yourselves."

And so it was that while the monks fetched water and food for the donkey and the camels, there was a knocking at the door. The merchants appeared in the doorway and looked in shyly. Then they asked whether their camels and the donkey had arrived there.

When Jerome approached them, they fell to their knees and begged him for forgiveness because they had now understood that the donkey had belonged to the monks and had been brought back by the lion. "We'll never do it again," they cried, "and we would like to make it up to you. We will give you half of the oil we are carrying with us, but please give us back our camels and hold off your lion because we have never been so terrified."

"I think that the lion was just as afraid when the donkey disappeared," said Jerome. "He has repaid you for that shock. But the donkey is back. That's the main thing, and we are very grateful to you for the oil."

When the merchants had fetched their camels, the lion lay down next to the donkey. He wanted to show that he would never again let it be stolen.

# George

## And fate chose the King's daughter

A great disaster had befallen the city of Silena in the country of Libya. The people of the town were being threatened by a venomous dragon which lived in the lake in front of the town. Whenever the dragon was hungry, it came out of the lake right up to the city walls and blew its fiery poisonous breath over the people and the animals so that they died. The inhabitants had often taken up arms against it, but every time it put them to flight. Then it would pursue them and devastate the land.

And so the poor citizens could not think of anything else to do but to give it two sheep every day. As long as it was given this offering, it kept quiet. But after a while the flocks of sheep had become so small that it was decided that the dragon could only have one sheep a day, as well as one inhabitant of the town. Every day the citizens drew lots to see who would be sacrificed to the dragon.

One day the lot fell on the king's daughter. The king sank into a profound gloom. He lamented bitterly and said to the people, "Take my possessions, my gold, my silver, or half my kingdom, but allow me to keep my only child. Do not let her be devoured by the terrible dragon."

The people were furious and cried out, "Many of our sons and daughters have already died, and you will not give up your daughter. This means you are breaking the law which you issued yourself. If you do not give up your daughter, we will burn you and your entire family." When the king saw that they were serious, he started to lament and called to the princess, "Oh my child, what shall I do? Woe is me, unhappy father. My only child must die." He went to the people again and said, "Give me another eight days so that I may bid her farewell. They allowed him to do this. However, on the eighth day, all the people congregated in front of his castle and called out angrily, "Why do you let your country be destroyed for the sake of your daughter? Must we all die from the poisonous breath of the dragon?"

At that moment the king realized that he could not save her. He called his servants to bring royal clothes and precious jewels, and dressed her like a princess. Then he embraced her and said, "I had hoped that you would bear children who would succeed to my throne. I also hoped that I would be able to attend your wedding when you married some noble knight. There would have been music in our palace and all the rulers of surrounding countries would have sat at our table. And now you must go and be devoured by the dragon."

He kissed her farewell and said, "It would have been better if I'd died before you."

However, she bent her head and knelt at her father's feet and asked for his blessing. And so he blessed her and she went forth. At the place where the dragon was waiting for her, she stood on the banks of the lake from where he was to appear. As she stood there, and the people on the city walls fearfully awaited the arrival of the dragon, a knight came riding towards them over the fields. He was riding a white horse and his harness shone in the light. He rode up to her and asked her why she was standing there.

"Lord," she said, "do not ask me that, but flee from here so you will not lose your life as well."

The knight replied, "Do not be afraid, daughter, but tell me what you are waiting for here, watched by the eyes of all your people."

She answered, "Lord, I can see that you have a good heart. But surely you do not wish to die with me. Flee as quickly as you can."

"I will not leave here," said the knight, "until you tell me why you are standing here weeping."

Then she told him everything about the dragon, about the years of struggle, about the sacrifices, and about herself, now that she had to die.

However, he said, "Dear princess, do not be afraid. I will help you in Christ's name."

She answered, "Good knight. You cannot do that. No one can vanquish the dragon. Why should you die with me?"

As they were talking to each other, the lake started to foam and boil and the dreadful head of the dragon emerged from the water. When the knight saw it, he sprang on to his horse and prepared himself for battle. The dragon went towards him blazing with fury. Then the knight made the sign of the Cross, seized his lance, called upon God's help, and spurred on his horse. The princess and the people on the city walls saw the knight bravely fighting the dragon, and finally wounding it so seriously with his lance that the beast crashed down on the shore.

The knight turned to the princess and said, "Now take your belt and tie it around the dragon's neck as a lead, and do not be afraid."

So she did this and the dragon followed her meekly. And so the knight and the princess and the dragon walked to the town and entered through the gate. The people screamed with fear and ran away in every direction to hide. They shouted, "Now we will all perish."

But the knight called upon them to come back, and said, "You should not be afraid. I am George, a fighter against evil. I conquered the dragon with the sign of the Cross. Because of this sign it has lost its power. If you would all like to receive this sign from me then I can kill the dragon and you will all be freed."

That is what happened. George made the sign of the Cross on everyone's forehead, and then he took his sword and killed the dragon. Four pairs of oxen were needed to drag the beast out of the town into the open field, where it was burned.

The king gave the knight gold and silver as a reward. However, he did not keep it for himself, but divided it amongst the people. Then he left and travelled on to perform other great deeds.

# on Sankt Barlaa
## und Josaphat

# Barlaam and Josaphat

## This is where I will be king

There was a king in India, called Avennir, who was a strict and just ruler. Moreover, he was so powerful that none of his enemies dared fight against him, and his people lived in peace. In addition, he was rich and everyone was in awe of him.

One day, the court of this great king was in complete turmoil. The chief councillor had unexpectedly left the court. Some people had seen him leave in the direction of the desert. Avennir sent soldiers after him with an order to bring him back to the court; he would not be punished, but the king wanted to hear from him and find out why he had left.

Finally, the soldiers returned with the councillor. They brought him to the throne and forced him to kneel down. Then the king gestured for them to leave. Avennir looked at him. Instead of his dignified silk robe he was wearing a coarsely woven habit. He had dispensed with his weapons. His head was bent slightly forward, but he did not seem to be afraid. Did he no longer respect the king? Everyone in court always bent down before him with his head down to the ground.

"Tell me where you went," said King Avennir, "and tell me the truth. I want to know. No harm will come to you. Stand up and speak!"

The councillor stood up and said, "Oh king, I went to the kingdom behind the desert. It is a country which borders directly on your own lands. I went there because I want to live there and serve the ruler of that country."

He told Avennir about that country. "Anyone who arrives at the gates must leave all the riches he owns there. Only the poor are allowed to enter. You must also put down all your weapons, because there is no war in that country. The fruit on the trees is our food and the water from the spring is our drink. The country is called Charis, and that means that no one owns anything themselves, but that everything is given to you every day."

Avennir asked, "And why do you prefer to live in that country rather than in mine? And who is the ruler you spoke of?"

The councillor replied, "Oh king, the years I had to serve you were past. I could go wherever I wanted. You made me rich, but this wealth worried me. I had to defend myself against thieves and robbers. I no longer wanted to do that. That is why I went to the land of Charis. The ruler who rules there gives everyone what he needs every day."

The king shook his head, and found it difficult to restrain his anger. "I promised you nothing would happen to you. I will not break that promise. However, your words are foolish. Go and live in a land of fools, and don't come back here."

The councillor left, and that evening the king stood on the highest tower of his castle. He saw his servant leave his country and go through the desert, and travel so far away that he lost him from sight.

Not long afterwards there was great joy in the castle. The Queen had borne a son, who was called Josaphat. It was their first child. There were great celebrations, because the king was no longer young and he would now have a successor for the throne.

Avennir had all the astrologers in his country come together. Thirty-five wise men came, and the king asked them what they could tell him about the newborn prince. Thirty-four of them bowed down deeply and said that they had read in the stars that the boy would become a worthy successor to his father.

However, one of them who was wiser than the rest stepped forward to the king and said, "My lord. He will become a king, but on a throne other than yours. The stars point towards the country of Charis, the country where no rich man may enter."

"But he is my successor," cried Avennir, "he must become king of my country. I will bind him to everything that is rich, healthy and strong."

The king set to work and had a castle built in the middle of the country. It was surrounded by a large garden with a high wall so that no one could look out over it. Only healthy, young servants were allowed to serve in this castle.

There was to be no lack of anything and the gates were guarded by heavily armed soldiers. Josaphat was taken to this castle, and the king ordered that he should never leave it.

The young prince grew up there, learning everything a prince should know and all the things he should be able to do. But the more he learned, the sadder he became. He learned about the world, but he could not know the world himself from behind the walls where he lived.

"Why can't I leave?" he asked again and again, and when his father realized at last how sad Josaphat was, he ordered that his son should be shown the area surrounding the palace.

The procession left on horseback, and in front of the procession there were servants who clapped their hands to drive away all the poor, sick and old people so that Josaphat would not see them.

However, one day they did meet a beggar after all. Josaphat reined in his horse, looked at him and asked his servant, "What sort of person is this?"

"This is a beggar," answered the servant.

"And why is he begging?" asked the prince.

"Because he does not have anything himself and must live on the gifts of others," the servant replied. Josaphat thought about this for a long time.

Another time there was a leper lying by the side of the road. Again the prince was surprised, and asked: "What happens when someone is ill?"

"It may be that he recovers, and it may be that he dies," the servant replied.

When they came across a quavering old man with wrinkled skin, Josaphat asked another question: "What happens to someone who is old?"

"One day, he will die," the servant answered.

Josaphat thought for a long time and then asked: "And what about me? Can I become sick? Will I grow old and die?"

The servant answered: "Yes, Lord, it is as you say."

In this way Josaphat learned to know the world and the people, and finally he asked: "You are all rich, healthy and strong. Are you happier than poor, sick, old and weak people?"

But the teachers and servants could not answer this question because they had not thought about it yet.

Then the wise old man, Barlaam, from the land of Charis, heard of the young prince's questions. He made his preparations and went to Josaphat. When Josaphat asked him these questions, he answered: "In the country where I live there are only poor people, and they are happy. Sick and old people also come to us, and many of them stay."

When Josaphat asked if he could see this country, Barlaam took him by the hand and led him through the desert to the land of Charis. At the gate he put down his sharp sword, took off his precious jewels and left his pieces of gold with the guard. He entered alone, and everyone he saw was just themselves, and lived without weapons, ornaments or money.

"This is where I wish to be king," said Josaphat. "This is my kingdom."

However, according to the legend, Barlaam told him that he must return to his own country, where his father reigned, and remain there until he found someone to become king in his place. Then he could go back to Barlaam.

And that is what happened. Josaphat returned many years later. He found Barlaam and from that time lived and ruled in the kingdom of Charis.

# Eustace

## You thought you would hunt me

Many centuries ago, there was a brave Roman general. His name was Placidus and he was the commander of the army under the Emperor Trajan. However, he was not only brave, but also a good and generous man, and many people placed their trust in him. In fact, God himself was to make him his servant when the time was ripe. And so it happened that one day, when he was hunting with his friends, a large deer leaped across his path and ran away to the most distant part of the forest where they were hunting. Placidus spurred on his horse and pursued the deer. He had seen it clearly; it was beautiful, and he wished to pursue it alone.

All day he spurred on his horse, following the trail of his quarry, and when the sun was low in the sky he saw the creature jumping on to a rock on the edge of a clearing in the forest. Placidus sharply reined in his horse and gazed at the creature. He thought of ways of catching it. As he was considering this, he suddenly saw a cross of light between the branches of the deer's antlers. He also thought he could see a human figure with arms outstretched on the Cross, and when he wondered what this was, the deer started speaking in a human voice and said: "Oh Placidus, you think you are pursuing me, but in fact I have come to you in the form of this deer. I am Christ, and without knowing it, you are serving me with your good deeds. You thought you were hunting me, but actually I've come for you."

Placidus was overwhelmed with fear and fell from his horse. For a long time he lay trembling on the ground. When he came to, he stood up. The deer was still standing there, and Placidus said: "I see the image of a cross lighter than the sun, and I can hear a human voice. Who is it that is talking to me?"

Then he heard Christ speak through the deer's mouth: "Placidus, I created heaven and earth, I divided light from darkness and made a distinction between day and night. I created man from the soil of the earth. I lived on earth as a man and died on the Cross, but I was stronger than death and conquered it."

Placidus said: "Lord, why have you come to me. What must I do?"

Christ answered: "Remember what I said, and ride home. Then go with your wife and two sons to the spring in the middle of this forest. Wash yourself in that spring, and rinse off everything which sticks to your body. Then come back to me tomorrow when light dawns, and let your wife and sons take part in all of this."

Placidus mounted his horse and rode back home. That night, he and his wife and sons washed in the spring and the next morning they returned to the rock. When he arrived, the deer with the antlers and the cross of light was there again, and said: "Placidus, from now on you will have a new name. You will be called Eustace, which means laden with fruit. However, you will suffer great hardships because you will henceforth be my servant; you will lose a great deal and you will not see me for a long time, but later I will come back to you and you will be given back everything you have lost."

Eustace bowed his head and said: "Yes Lord, I would like to serve and follow you, but I ask you to give me the strength to do this."

Then he turned back home. Soon afterwards, a disease spread amongst his servants and they all died. His cattle also fell sick and perished. Thieves broke into his house and farm and stole all the valuables they could find.

When Eustace and his wife had nothing left, they felt ashamed and withdrew from society. They left their home and travelled to a port where they embarked on a ship and sailed to Egypt.

However, on the way the captain noticed Theospite, Eustace's wife, and saw that she was beautiful. When the ship arrived in Egypt, he demanded the payment for the journey from Eustace, and when it became clear that Eustace could not pay, the captain took Theospite and told Eustace: "If you do not give me the money you owe me, I will take your wife."

Eustace would not agree to this, but when he continued to object, the captain called his crew to him and said: "I demand Eustace's wife instead of payment. If he continues to object, seize him and throw him into the sea."

Then Eustace bent his head, bade farewell to Theospite and disembarked from the ship with his two sons. He travelled inland, full of sorrow for his wife, whom he had had to leave with a strange man.

They soon came to a broad river which they had to cross. The water was so deep that Eustace did not dare wade across with both children at once. So he left one behind on the bank and took the other and carried him across the river to the other side. He left him there and then he went back again to fetch his brother. When he was in the middle of the river he heard his child crying behind him. He turned around and saw that a wolf had come up, seized the child and bounded off into the woods and disappeared with him. When he tried to go back to help him, he heard a cry from the other bank. He turned round again, and this time saw that a huge lion had picked up his other child and had run away so quickly that he only caught a glimpse of it.

He stood in the middle of the big river in utter despair, hoping to be drowned, because he was so sad about what had happened to his children, and because he was now all alone in this strange land. But he remembered the words which the deer had spoken to him, and so he took courage and waded through the river to the opposite bank. Finally, he came to a village, where he accepted work with a farmer, looking after the horses.

However, he had not realized that there had been peasants working on the river bank when the wolf had run off with his son. They chased the wolf, saved the child, and took it to the village where they lived. On the other bank, shepherds were tending their sheep. They shouted when the lion came, waved their sticks and set their dogs on the beast, so that it let the child go and fled. They too took the child with them to the village where they lived.

Thus the boys grew up in the same village, though they did not know that they were brothers. Eustace lived in another village and worked there for many years. His wife Theospite was not with the captain for very long. He fell ill and died soon afterwards, so that she was free again and got a job serving in a tavern.

Fifteen years later, war broke out in the Roman Empire once again. The Emperor had lost a great battle, and remembered that many years before he had had a commander called Placidus, who had won all his wars. One day he had suddenly disappeared and after that, no one had ever seen him again. The Emperor wanted Placidus to command the army again, and sent soldiers to look for him in every corner of his empire.

One day, as Eustace was working on the farm, he saw two men approaching across the fields. He looked at them and saw that they were two soldiers from his army. When he recognized them, he suddenly remembered his earlier life. He thought of his wife whom he had lost, his sons, whom he believed to be dead, and all the good and

beautiful things which he used to have when he was still a commander. He gave a deep sigh and tears of sadness filled his eyes. Then he
heard a familiar voice speaking to him: "Eustace, have courage. In a
very short while everything will come back to you."

When he looked up, the men were standing before him. They
greeted him and asked him if he knew anyone called Placidus. He
told them he didn't, and invited them to come in to drink a glass of
water. While he was fetching the water, the soldiers agreed that this
stable-hand looked just like their former commander, and when he
gave them their water, they would look to see whether he had a scar
on his forehead which he had received from an injury on the battle-
field. When he came back, they saw that he had the scar, and Eustace had to admit that he was the one they were looking for. They
jumped up and embraced him, full of joy that they had found him,
dressed him in splendid clothes and took him to Rome.

The Emperor himself rode up to meet him. He welcomed him
joyfully and placed him in command of his troops, However, when
Eustace saw his army, he realized that there were not enough soldiers
to defeat the enemy. He sent messengers out to every part of the
Empire, and every village and town was obliged to provide strong
men for the army.

The village where Eustace's sons had grown up also had to send
two men, and the two brothers were singled out as being the
strongest and bravest. When they joined the army, Eustace was glad
to see them and placed them directly under his own command.

The battle was fought and the Romans won a great victory. On the
trip back to Rome the two young men spent the night in the small
inn where their mother was serving. However, they did not know that
she was their mother. In fact, they did not even know that they were
brothers.

That evening, after dinner, one of the brothers started talking about
his early experiences. The woman at the inn sat at the table and
listened.

"When I was small," he said, "my father and mother left our home
with my younger brother and myself. We sailed across the sea. When
we landed, we went on, but my mother remained on the ship — I
don't know why. Then my father carried my younger brother across
a big river, put him down on the other side, and went back to fetch
me. When he was in the middle of the river, a wolf appeared on the
other side, seized my brother and ran off with him. Immediately afterwards, a lion jumped on me, seized me and tried to take me away,

but I was rescued by shepherds. I don't know what happened to my father and my brother, I never heard from them again."

Then the other young man exclaimed: "But I heard that I was saved from the jaws of a wolf by peasants. We must be brothers."

They embraced and wept tears of joy because they had found each other.

Meanwhile, the woman had been listening attentively, and thought: "These could be my two sons." She went to the commander to ask him what he knew about the two young men, but when she stood before him, she saw the scar on his forehead and recognized him as her husband. She bowed down before him and said: "Lord, tell me what you have done in your life up to now, because I suspect that you are Placidus, the commander who also bears the name Eustace, to whom the deer with the cross of light appeared, and who became a servant of Christ. I am his wife, who had to be left behind on the ship. He also had two sons, whom he took with him when he left me behind."

When Eustace heard this, he looked closely at her and saw that it was his own wife Theospite who was talking to him. They recognized each other and embraced and wept with joy.

"Lord," Theospite asked then, "where are your two sons?"

"They were seized by wild animals," he answered, and told her what had happened. Then she took him with her and showed him the two young men. And so they also found their sons.

And they built a new house in the place where they had been before and lived there together happily from then on.

# Elizabeth of Hungary

## Pure red roses

Elizabeth was the daughter of the King of Hungary. Everyone loved her when she was a little girl living in the royal castle. The courtiers and guests brought her the best food, the most beautiful presents and the most wonderful toys. Her parents looked after her as well as they could, and it was said that she was even bathed in a tub made of pure silver.

When she had learned to walk, her nurse Adelheide often took her out for a walk. They would go down the road from the fortress at the top of the mountain to the villages, where peasants, craftsmen and merchants lived. There were children playing there, and when Elizabeth passed, they would stop playing and would greet her and Adelheide. Some stretched out their hands and said: "I'm hungry. Do you have anything to eat?"

Elizabeth knew the children in the castle, who were strong and well fed. Now she saw that the village children were thin, and she became aware that they did not have enough to eat.

Elizabeth often thought about the village children, and one day she decided to go down to look in the kitchen. She walked through the long corridors, went down the stone staircase and carefully opened the heavy kitchen door. She saw that there were all sorts of good things to eat, and looked around curiously, taking everything in. Suddenly she smelled the fragrance of freshly baked bread, and she went to the corner of the kitchen where some round brown rolls had just come out of the oven.

She remembered the pale children who had said they were hungry and saw what she needed here. Quickly she lifted up her pinafore with one hand and put in a few rolls with the other. Then she ran out of the kitchen, back up the stairs and through the corridors. However, the cook had seen her and ran after her. When he was just behind her, the door into the corridor opened and Elizabeth's mother, the Queen, appeared in the doorway. Elizabeth looked up and tripped in her confusion. She let go of her pinafore and what happened then was completely unexpected.

It was not the rolls that fell out of her pinafore, but pure red roses. One after the other, they cascaded to the ground and their fragrance spread throughout the corridor and then the whole castle. The cook picked up a rose in astonishment and took it to the kitchen. The Queen helped her daughter up and gave the roses to a servant, ordering him to take them to the poor as a gift from little Elizabeth.

## John the Baptist

Not long afterwards, a number of important knights and noblewomen visited the Hungarian castle. They came with instructions to fetch Elizabeth. She was to marry the son of the Count of Thüringen.

A large farewell party was held, and Elizabeth left with the knights and the noblewomen and set off for the great castle at Wartburg in Germany.

In that country people spoke a different language, and it was a long time before Elizabeth could understand and speak it. All that time, and for many years afterwards, she looked for someone to whom she could really talk easily.

One day, she was sitting in the small chapel of the castle. Before her stood the altar with seven burning candles. This was just as it had been at home with her parents, but she still felt that she needed someone to talk to.

Then she noticed a big man with a serious face standing by the altar. She saw that he was wearing a brown robe and a leather belt. He had long, dark hair, his face was austere, but the eyes that looked at her were friendly.

Suddenly she heard that he was talking to her in her own language, and tears of joy came into her eyes. He placed three white candles in her hands and said: "Elizabeth, read the name on these candles. It's my name. In future, if you call on this name, I will be with you. You will never be lonely again, whatever happens."

When Elizabeth looked at the candles, she saw the name, John the Baptist, on each candle. She looked at him again, and said softly: "John the Baptist?"

"Yes," he said, "I'm John the Baptist. Think of me, and nothing will be too much for you."

Her eyes moved back to the three candles in her hands, and when she looked up, he had disappeared.

She took them with her to her room. When she felt alone or sad, she lit them, all three in a row, and as long as she lived, they never burned down.

## Ludwig and Elizabeth

The son of the Count of Thüringen, Ludwig, was growing up fast. Everyone in the castle was aware that, on reaching manhood, he was to marry Elizabeth.

One day, a young lion escaped from its cage in the city square and was pacing to and fro, roaring. The people cried out in fear and hid behind the doors of the castle. However, Ludwig walked into the square and went straight up to the lion. He looked at it and commanded it sternly to go back into its cage. The lion obeyed, went into its cage and the door was shut behind it.

Then the people knew that Ludwig had now really reached manhood. This meant that the time had come for him to take Elizabeth as his wife. Before he did this, he sent her a gift. It was a hand mirror with two faces. On one side it was a mirror in which you could see your own face; on the other side, there was an image of Christ. Elizabeth thanked Ludwig for this gift, and they were married not long afterwards.

She often used the mirror, and when she wanted to see herself, she first looked at the image on the back, and then at herself. This meant that her own face became beautiful and pure.

## More roses

There were often poor people living in the houses around the castle of Wartburg. Elizabeth constantly went down the long road to help them, to nurse them and to bring them bread. Increasingly the knights and noblewomen in the castle mocked her, and accused her of taking their food to give to these people.

"Do you want us to be just as poor as they are?" they chided her.

"If it were up to me," she answered, "I would not be richer than they are." And so she gave them not only the food, but also her own clothes.

One day, as she was leaving the castle and going down the road to the houses of the poor, Ludwig followed her on his horse. He caught up with her, reined in his horse, bent forward, took her cloak and pulled it back to see what she had taken from the castle. Just as the

Hungarian queen and the cook had once seen the little princess's roses, her husband Ludwig now discovered roses under her cloak. With the morning sun shining on them, the red and pink colours contrasted strikingly with the white dress she was wearing.

Ludwig sprang from his horse, placed the cloak around her and kissed her. "Take the people as many roses as you like," he said, "I'll never ask you about it again." And he rode back to the castle.

## The leper

The people had merely mocked and accused her when she took bread from the castle, but they became really furious and cursed her when she brought in the sick from the streets. Once she found a leper by the side of the road, and, full of pity, she brought him back with her. She led him into the castle and took him up the stairs to her room. Then she washed him and gave him something to eat. Finally, she put him to bed in the bed where she always slept with Ludwig.

The people in the castle thought it was scandalous, because they believed that leprosy was a contagious disease and therefore everyone in the neighbourhood could be infected. When Lord Ludwig came home that evening, they took him to his room to show him what Elizabeth had done. She sat quietly in a corner. Ludwig walked to their bed and removed the counterpane to see whether what his servants said was true; that his wife had given their bed to a leper. But when he pulled back the blankets, he knelt down in awe. What he saw was not a diseased man from the streets, but the most beautiful person in the world. He saw Christ Himself, surrounded by an aura of light so pure that Ludwig remained kneeling, looking at the sight for a long time.

Then he covered Him up, turned to Elizabeth and said: "Through your act I was able to see Him."

## The emperor

The guard on the highest tower of the castle of Wartburg leant forward, peering intently at the plain below him. He could see a cloud of dust and a large group of knights in colourful cloaks. Then he recognized the coat of arms of the German Emperor on the first flag, and at the same time he saw that the knights had turned into the road leading up to the castle. Did anyone know anything about this visit? He seized hold of his horn and gave the piercing signal thrice.

The people of Wartburg stirred and the news soon spread from mouth to mouth: "The Emperor is approaching. He is paying us an unexpected visit; he could be here within the hour."

Then Ludwig arrived and issued his commands. The whole house was rapidly cleaned. The cooks in the kitchen hurriedly started work. The largest table in the banqueting hall was laid and a banquet was prepared. Then everyone hurried to their rooms and dressed in their best clothes. Just as all this had happened, the trumpet sounded at the head of the procession which appeared at the doorway. The women and children looked out of the windows, down on to the courtyard where the Emperor himself rode in, followed by all his men on horseback, one after the other.

They were all warmly welcomed, and the important guests followed the lord of the castle to the great hall, where everyone entered wearing their best clothes. When they had all taken their places, the noblemen were embarrassed to see the empty chair next to the Emperor where Elizabeth should have been sitting. It remained empty when they all sat down.

But then a page opened the door and Elizabeth appeared. The bustle in the hall subsided, everyone fell silent and looked in amazement at the Countess as she came in and took her place next to the Emperor. What had happened?

Elizabeth had heard of the Emperor's arrival at the very last moment. Hurriedly she looked for an appropriate garment to wear for the celebration, but she could not find anything. She had given everything to the poor. She no longer possessed anything other than her ordinary everyday clothes. She felt deeply ashamed, especially on Ludwig's behalf. In her distress she went to the chapel and knelt down. She asked God to grant it that she might appear worthy. Elizabeth knew that anyone who truly asks God for something will receive it.

Thus the guests and the inhabitants of the castle saw her enter, dressed in a cloak of shining light. She had never been so beautiful. She sat down next to the Emperor, and everyone who looked at her felt a great happiness in their hearts.

Then evening fell and the meal came to an end. The important guests left the castle, but the memory of Elizabeth stayed with them forever.

## Francis's cloak

One day, Brother Francis of Assisi stood before Cardinal Ugolino in Italy, a long way from the castle in Wartburg. "Francis," asked the Cardinal, "do you know Sister Elizabeth? She comforts and cures people just like you do. She trusts in God's help, just as you do. She is your true sister, but you know, Francis, things are not easy for her. The people are often cruel and horrible to her. Wouldn't you like to help your sister? She'd be grateful if you gave her your cloak."

And so, one day a messenger brought Elizabeth Francis's cloak. This made her very happy. Whenever she went into the chapel to ask a question, she would always put on Francis's warm brown cloak. It made her feel that a long way away she had a friend and brother. This gave her strength and a sense of peace.

## We are waiting for you

At the end of her life, Elizabeth lived in Marburg in a house where she nursed the sick. She worked hard because she felt that she did not have much time left. She also had to rest more often because she found the work increasingly hard. One evening she was sitting by the window after a long day. She was tired from working, and looked out.

Then she saw a man coming towards her. Was it the leper whom she had put in her own bed, or was it Christ Himself? He came to her and pointed up at the clouds. Elizabeth raised up her eyes and saw that a great banquet had been prepared up above the clouds.

The man said to her: "It is time. We are waiting for you. Are you coming with me?"

"Yes," said Elizabeth, "I am coming with you and I would like to celebrate the banquet with you."

When she had gone, the people saw that birds were flying in from every direction. They sang more beautifully than ever before, in honour of Elizabeth and what she had done in her life for the poor and the sick.

Cristofori faciem die quanicunque tueris
Illa nempe die morte mala non morieris

Millesimo ccccᵒ
xxᵒ anno

# Christopher

## If you wait long enough

Once upon a time a man called Offerus lived in the country of Canaan. He was a giant and tremendously strong. The king of his country wished him to be his servant because he performed the work of many labourers, and in wartime he was a mighty warrior. However, he had decided to serve only the greatest of kings.

He travelled through many lands until he found the king who was said to be mightiest of all. This king saw the giant standing before his throne and joyfully employed him, because kings can always use strong servants. And so Offerus worked there, until one evening a feast was held in the palace. Offerus was also invited. After eating and drinking a great deal, a singer performed who told a story while he played his lute. It was an exciting story and everyone listened quietly. However, Offerus saw that at some points during the story the king made the sign of the Cross and he noticed that the king also did this every time the storyteller spoke about the Devil. Was he afraid of something?

When the feast was over he went to the king and asked why had he done this. The king did not wish to answer him, but Offerus said that he wanted to know, and that he would not continue to serve the king unless he told him. So the king had to admit that he was afraid of the Devil and wished to protect himself against the Devil with the sign of the Cross. "So is the Devil mightier than you?" asked Offerus. The king had to agree that this was so. "Then I cannot serve you any longer," said Offerus, "because I wish to offer my services to the mightiest lord of all."

And so he bade farewell to his king and went in search of the Devil. Before long he arrived in a bare and desolate region. A winding road led between the sandy hills, and suddenly he encountered a group of knights, one of whom looked very wild and terrifying. This knight went up to him and asked him what he wanted. "I'm looking for Lord Devil," answered Offerus. "Then you've come to the right place because I am the Devil myself. What do you want with me?"

"I wish to serve the strongest lord," said Offerus, "and I believe you are the strongest."

"Of course I am," grimaced the knight. "Just come along with me."

And so Offerus followed the Devil but not long afterwards, they were walking down a straight road when the Devil saw a cross by the side of the road. He shrank back, veered away from the road and clambered over rocks and winding paths with Offerus until he rejoined the main road a long way further on. "Tell me," said Offerus, "why are you making this detour? Is something troubling you?"

"Me, troubled by something? What on earth do you mean?" shouted the Devil, but as they walked on, he peered left and right to see if there might be another cross by the road. "You were afraid of that cross," said Offerus. "Why was that?"

Now the Devil could no longer deny it, and had to admit that the Cross is the sign of Christ and that he could not endure that sign.

"In that case, Christ is stronger than you," said Offerus, "and as I wish to serve the strongest lord, I am leaving your service. I will go and seek Christ." When he heard the word "Christ," the Devil pulled a face, looked round fearfully and fled.

Offerus went on his way, and after a long search he found a lonely hermit. The people had told him that he would able to help him. When the hermit saw the mighty Offerus approaching, he opened the door of his hut and bade him enter. Bending down, Offerus entered through the door and sat down on some of the straw lying about, his back to the wall of the hut.

"If you want to find Christ, you will have to fast for a long time," said the hermit.

"Fast?" Offerus replied anxiously, and he sat up against the wall so that the hut creaked. "I can't fast."

"And you will have to pray a great deal," the hermit added.

"I've never heard of praying," sighed Offerus, "I wish to serve Christ, I want to do something about it."

The hermit had to think about this, but after a while he indicated that Offerus should go outside with him. Then he pointed down to the valley where they could hear a river rushing in the distance. "Down there," he said, "is a river where travellers often wish to cross to the other side. But there is no bridge, and the water flows so turbulently that many people have perished. You are so big and strong that you could carry the people across. If you do that long enough, then one day Christ will be one of those travellers. In this way you will be able to meet him."

This seemed like a good plan to Offerus. He walked down the hill to the river. It foamed turbulently, but he was not afraid. He built a hut on the bank of the river to live in. He also found a strong straight staff to help him cross the river, and in this way he started on his task.

For many years he carried travellers over the river and they always crossed safely to the other side. Nothing was too much for him, and he gratefully accepted everything people gave him for his services. When he became impatient or disappointed that it took so long to wait for Christ, the hermit consoled him and told him to continue with his task and persevere.

And so it happened that after many years Offerus was resting in his hut one day when he heard a child's voice calling outside: "Come outside and take me across."

He went outside and looked left and right, but didn't see anyone. Then he went back inside. However, once again he heard the same voice calling him, and again he could not find anyone. When he heard the voice for the third time and obediently went outside again to see who was calling him, he saw a child standing there, asking to be taken across the river.

Offerus put the child on his shoulders, took his staff and started to cross the river. But when he went into the water, the river started to flood. The water rose and rose and the child was as heavy as lead. The further he went into the river, the higher the water rose, and the heavier the child pressed down on his shoulders. He was afraid that he would drown when he waded through the middle of the river. When he reached the other shore, using every last ounce of strength, he put down the child and said to him, "You placed me in great danger. You were so heavy that the whole world could not have weighed more than you."

The child answered, "You should not be surprised about that, Offerus, because you not only carried the whole world on your shoulders, but also the One who created the world. You should know that I am Christ, your King, whom you are serving with this work, and because you carried me you will be given a new name. Up to now you have been called Offerus, which means 'bearer.' From now on you will be called Christopher, which means, 'the bearer of Christ.' I ask you to take your staff and place it in the ground when you get back home, so that you can see that I am speaking the truth. Next morning it will bear leaves and fruit."

After these words the child disappeared from sight.

Christopher went back through the river. When he arrived at his hut, he planted his staff in the ground, and when he got up next morning it had borne leaves and fruit. Then he knew that he had become the servant of the greatest King of all.

# Martin

## Aren't you afraid?

Once upon a time there was a Roman general. He had a son, Martin, and he expected him to become the commander of an army as well. But Martin had other ideas. "Why should I kill people with swords or spears," he thought. "I want them to live, not die." When the father heard that Martin did not wish to join the army, he was very angry. He had soldiers come to fetch him. They tied his hands and feet, placed him on a cart and carried him off to the army. At this time he was fifteen years old and had to serve as a soldier for three years. Then he would be free.

### Near Amiens

One winter's day, Martin came to the city of Amiens. By the city gates he saw a poor beggar who was shivering with cold because he had no clothes to put on. But Martin had only the clothes he was wearing because he had given away all his other clothes.

He looked at the beggar and saw the inhabitants of the town and the soldiers walking past him, leaving him standing in the icy cold. Then he took his own cloak and cut it in two with his sword. He gave one half to the beggar and put the other half around his shoulders.

When he rode on, there were people who laughed at him because he did not look very chivalrous, wearing half a cloak; but others admired him for what he had done.

That night he had a dream. He saw Christ dressed in the half cloak that he had given to the beggar, standing before him, surrounded by angels. Christ said to the angels: "Look, Martin gave me this cloak. He is still young and yet he has already done this deed." Not long afterwards, Martin was baptized, but he continued to serve as a soldier in the army because he wished to fulfil his duty to the Emperor.

When his time as a soldier had almost come to an end, there was a new commander of the army. He was called Julianus.

This commander called together his loyal leaders and gave them each a piece of gold. "Tomorrow will be a heavy day," he told them. "The enemy will attack our country from Gaul, and we will have to fight a difficult battle. I am giving you this gold as proof of my faith in you."

But Martin did not wish to accept the gift. He did not wish to fight the battle against the Gauls, and he thought, "I've served my time. My task as a soldier has been completed." He went to Julianus and told him this.

Julianus was very angry and shouted, "You're a coward. You're leaving because you're afraid of the enemy!" Martin would not accept this.

"I'll show you that I'm not afraid, and that I'm not leaving the army because I'm a coward. Tomorrow morning before the start of the battle, I'll walk out to meet the enemy in front of the army, without my armour, my helmet, my sword or my shield. I will carry only the wooden cross which I always have with me."

The men who were there and knew him looked at him with great admiration, but Julianus shouted: "Take him and lock him up. Then bring him to the head of the army tomorrow morning. We will see what the enemy does to a fool with a wooden cross."

So Martin was led away.

The following morning the Roman soldiers saw what the enemy did. Even before the army had drawn up, a Gallic horseman galloped up early in the morning. He carried a white pennant fluttering in the wind, because he was a messenger of peace and carried a message that the Gallic army had retreated during the night.

Martin was now a free man. He had served as a soldier for three years. He lay down his arms, took off his soldier's uniform and left the army for good.

## Amongst robbers

He wished to see his father and mother again. He wanted to tell them about the dream he had had in Amiens, and about the Gauls who had withdrawn when he promised to meet them unarmed. So he set off to see them.

To find his parents, he had to cross the Alps. He passed through lonely and desolate regions, the trees became sparser and sparser and the bare grey mountains rose up in front of him. Suddenly five men jumped out at him. They seized him and pulled him into a cave by the side of the road. They took everything he owned, and when they had done that, one of the robbers raised a huge axe to kill him. However, another robber held this man's arm and prevented him from hitting Martin. Then they tied him up and the robber who had saved Martin stayed with him to guard him. All the others left.

For a while the two men sat silently in the cave, and then the robber turned to Martin and said, "My friend wanted to hit you with the axe and I saw that you sat there quietly. Weren't you afraid?"

"No," said Martin, "I was not afraid."

"Why is that?" asked the robber. "I'm afraid when someone wishes to hurt me."

"It is a great secret," replied Martin, "but as you asked me, I would like to tell you. This is the secret: the greater the danger we are in, the closer we are to God, and God is the strongest protector. That is why I had never been so safe as when your friend raised his axe against me."

Then Martin taught him how to find this protection, and the robber was so grateful that he took off the shackles and brought him to his parents by the right road.

Martin visited his mother and father and told them about his experiences. They said: "You are an even braver soldier than we thought."

Then they parted and bade each other farewell.

## The Emperor

Years later, Martin had built a large house for the sick and the poor, together with his fellow monks. Then he heard that the Emperor was sending soldiers to tear down this house because it was in his way. He decided to go to the Emperor and to ask him if he could keep the house.

When he arrived at the Emperor's castle after a long journey, the Emperor had already heard that he was coming and did not wish to receive him. So Martin arrived to find the doors closed, and no one would let him in. The next day he tried again, and the day after that. But the door remained locked and no one answered when he knocked.

Then he said: "I do not come for myself. I come for my brothers, the sick and the poor. Is there no one who can help me?"

Suddenly he saw an angel standing in front of him. "I am the angel of the sick and the poor. Trust in me," said the angel. He touched the door and it opened. Then Martin followed the angel through the corridors and up the staircases of the castle to the Emperor's room. Martin went up to the Emperor, but the Emperor flew into a rage and wanted to chase him away. Then the angel made a pillar of fire flame up before the throne so that the Emperor jumped up fearfully and called out, "Martin, ask what you like and it will be granted." This is how the Emperor listened to Martin, and Martin was able to keep his house. He thanked the angel many times afterwards for opening the doors for him and making the Emperor listen to him.

## The knights

Once Martin was riding along the road on his small grey donkey. Three knights approached on horseback from the other direction. The wind blew up Martin's cloak so that it flapped sideways at the knights. Their horses were frightened, and the knights thought Martin should be punished. They jumped down, seized him and started to use their whips on him. He did not defend himself and they became even more furious, and hit him harder. At last they let him go, and went back to their horses.

However, when they took the horses' reins, the creatures stood completely still and the knights could not move them from their places. The knights cursed their horses but could not get them to move. They pulled and yanked and hit them with their whips, but nothing happened. Their fury turned to concern, and they looked anxiously at Martin, who was still sitting by the side of the road next to his donkey. Finally, they went up to him with bowed heads and said to him they were very sorry they had beaten him so severely.

"If you're truly sorry, then it's alright. Your horses are free and you can go."

## The St Martin's goose

For the following years Martin lived in the town of Marmoutiers in France. Many people came to see him. He gave food to the hungry, and cured the sick. The people liked to visit him so much that they no longer wished to leave. They found somewhere nearby to live.

"Wouldn't you like to become a Bishop?" they asked him once. "Oh no," he answered, "never. I would like to stay here with the poor and the sick. This where I am happy." But one day the bishop in that area died and had to be replaced by a new one. No one doubted who should replace him — they all wanted Martin to become the bishop — and so hundreds of people went together to see him to make him the bishop, whether he wanted this or not. Martin heard them coming and he knew what they wanted. However, he did not think he was worthy to become bishop, and so he walked quietly out of his house by the back door, opened the goose pen and hid in their hut behind the trough.

When the people arrived, they couldn't find him and were surprised and disappointed. One of them called out,

"Martin!" And then many people called out: "Martin, where are you?"

But he kept quiet and did not say anything.

Finally, they all called out as loudly as they could and listened to find out whether he would answer after all. At that moment they saw one of the geese emerging from the goose pen, honking and with its neck outstretched. Then it went back to the place where Martin was hiding. Of course, he was discovered, and was made bishop against his wishes.

Thus he had been betrayed by a goose, and that is why in some regions a goose is cooked on St Martin's Day, and this is known as the St Martin's goose.

## The men in the white cloaks

Now that Martin was old, he often sat on his three-legged stool which he always used. He would look at the sky, and when his brothers asked him why he did this, he kept silent.

When the time came for him to leave the earth, he asked to be placed on the floor without any straw or mattress. He did not want to lie on his side, but always on his back.

"Let me look up at heaven," he said, "and not down at the earth, because the gates of heaven are slowly opening for me." When evening had fallen, the window of the room where he lay was wide open. Men in white cloaks came and took him up. They carried him to the river and laid him in their boat. Then they cast off from the banks and sailed downriver with Martin towards the wide sea.

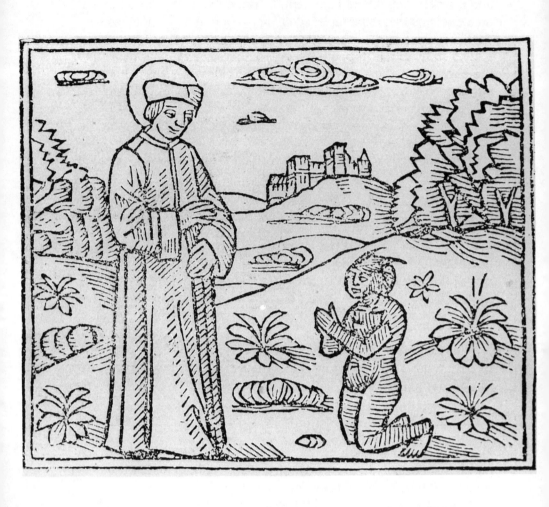

# Antony of Egypt

## I have come for my friend

Antony was only twenty years old, and yet he was already a rich man. His parents had both died, and he had inherited their entire fortune. He owned many houses and estates, and he had gold and gems, as well as cupboards full of fine clothes. The people living round about saw him appear in different costly outfits and admired him because he was noble and important. The farmers who lived on his estates obeyed him because he was just and honest. Everyone treated him with respect.

In fact, this made him all the more lonely, and he increasingly had a feeling that something was lacking, something which might be the most important thing of all. "I would so much like to have a friend," he said to himself from time to time. And this idea developed in him to become a strong longing for a true friend.

One day, someone knocked at the door of his house. It was a quiet, gentle knock. Antony thought it must be a beggar. Beggars came to the house constantly all day long. It was as though they were always hungry and expected him to be ready for them at any time. Angry at being disturbed, he pretended not to hear anything.

That night he had a dream. He dreamt that there was a man at his front door who asked him, "Why didn't you open the door to me today?"

Antony was frightened and asked, "Was it you knocking at the door?"

"Yes," said the man, "and I came because you asked me to come. I would like to be your friend, but your door was shut and I could not come in."

"I'm sorry," said Antony, "but what can I do in order to become your friend?"

The man answered, "I am Christ, and anyone who wishes to be my friend must give everything they own to the poor. That is what I am asking you to do. When you no longer have a house to shut yourself up in, I will always be able to come to you. So when you have given everything away, come and follow me."

When Christ had said this, he turned around, walked out of the house through the village, and then up the road to the desert. Antony saw him walking through the desert before he disappeared behind a hill. When Antony realized that he had gone, he wanted to jump up and run after him so that he could stay with him and then ... he woke up with a start.

It was still very early in the morning, but he was burning with desire to do what he had been told. He got up and first went to the farmers on his estate. He gave every one of them a house and some land. When he returned home, he started to divide up his possessions amongst the poor in the village, and he gave the house where he had lived himself to his steward. Before evening fell, everything had been divided up, and he left the village and walked towards the desert. When darkness fell he found an empty hut on the edge of the desert and went in to spend the night there.

The people were surprised by what he had done, but they were also grateful for the many things he had given them, and every day they came to visit him with food and drink.

One day, he dreamt that he was standing in the doorway of his hut looking out over the desert. In the distance between the yellowish-red sand and the bright, white chalky hills, he saw a dark cave. He saw Christ walking up the road to the cave and then going into it.

When he woke up the next morning, he realized that he should follow his friend even further. Did Christ actually live in that cave? He left his hut and travelled further. It was a long journey. Again it was almost dark when he arrived at the cave, and he decided to go inside for the night.

He sat down on the ground and his eyes became used to the darkness, but to his horror he saw that he was surrounded on all sides by the most dreadful creatures. He had never seen such creatures before. They started to move towards him, hissing and growling at him: "What are you doing here? There's nothing for you here. Get out of here!"

But Antony knew that Christ had gone in, and he was determined to follow him. He said, "I have come for my friend I will not leave."

"This is our cave. Go away or we will devour you." The beasts went up to him hissing, screeching and roaring, and stretching out their claws. However, Antony knew that he must not retreat, and he stayed where he was. Then the wild beasts sprang up from every side and leapt at him. They pulled him over the ground by his hair. They bit and scratched, and they kicked him with their hooves.

This went on for a long time and he suffered great agonies. But suddenly he thought of his friend. Where could he be? Had he abandoned him? Surely it was his friend who had beckoned him to come and to go into this cave? When he asked himself these questions, the darkness lit up with a soft glow. The creatures crawled back to the walls and disappeared in the holes and cracks in the cave. His pain eased and he looked up.

He realized that his friend was with him, and he said, "Jesus! Where were You all that time while I was being tortured?"

"Antony, I was close by," answered Jesus, "but I wanted to know whether you truly wished to follow me. Now that I have seen that you can fight bravely, I know that I can trust in you."

For many years Antony lived in this cave and the monsters never returned. Then he knew that the time had come for him to move on. This time his journey passed through the desert for many days, until he came to a place so far away from people that they could no longer bring him food and drink. It was a small oasis where he stayed, with a clear spring and fertile land all around. There was shade under the palm trees that grew there. Antony tilled the land around the spring and grew vegetables and cereals in his fields. He lived for many years from the produce he grew on this land. Many animals came to see him, and some of them wished to trample his wheat, but he would go to them and talk to them strictly. They did not fight back, but listened to him and left again.

When he was ninety years old, he heard that there was another hermit called Paul, living deep in the wilderness. He wished to go and visit him, but after he had left on the long journey, the path petered out and he no longer knew in which direction to travel. He had proved that he was not afraid of wild animals, and had also shown that he would not hurt them, and therefore they trusted him and wished to help him.

A big grey wolf came through the woods towards him and walked in front of him, straight through the wilderness, until they came to the hut of the old hermit, Paul. Antony thanked the wolf and knocked on the hermit's door until he appeared. The two men were together for a long time and talked to each other. A deer came out of the bushes and lay down at Paul's feet, and when it was time to eat, a raven flew up to them with two pieces of bread.

When Antony expressed his surprise, Paul said, "Whenever it's time to eat, this raven brings me my bread. Today it has brought two pieces."

Then they broke bread together and ate half of the bread each. Afterwards, Antony returned to his oasis.

One day, when he was very old — it is said that he reached the age of 105 — he was sitting in the doorway of his hut in the oasis when Christ appeared to him. He said, "Stand up and come to me." Antony did so. "Now take off the clothes you have always worn and take this cloak which I have brought for you."

Antony did so and saw that he was now wearing a shining blue cloak, as blue as heaven itself.

"This is my gift to you," said Christ. "You have given all your possessions and all your beautiful clothes to the poor. Now you are wearing a garment which you will never take off, and it will never become stained or wear out. Everyone will see that my friend Antony wears the cloak that I have given him."

And Christ took him by the hand and led him to the place in heaven where everyone goes when they have completed their work on earth.

# Patrick

## Because you did not forget my name

An old man sat on the top of a hill in the country of Erin. His hair was silvery grey and the locks grew down to his shoulders. However, when you looked into his clear blue eyes, you saw a man in his prime, for they radiated courage and joy.

He often sat in this peace. The hill sloped down to a round, tranquil lake which was surrounded by other similar hills. He liked to look out over the water, which reflected everything: the trees, the clouds, the green grass and the blue sky. When he sat there, he thought about the things which he had experienced in his long life.

Once, when he was a young man, he had met someone whom he knew to be his master. This man had said to him, "Patrick, find the most beautiful country on earth. Even if you spend all your life looking for it, don't rest until you've found it."

When the master had said this and had gone, Patrick started to travel through many countries. Now that he was an old man, he could look back at everything he had seen, and that was a lot. He had also wandered far and wide in that land of Erin. It was his favourite country, but he knew there must be something else which he had not yet found.

Thinking about these things, his gaze passed over the lake and the hills and he became so engaged that he didn't notice a shepherd coming towards him and sitting down next to him. Patrick looked up at him, and very slowly a memory rose up in him as though rising up from deep water. The shepherd was silent, and waited until Patrick finally said in amazement, "Master, you have come to me."

"Yes," answered the shepherd, "I wanted to hear from you whether you have found the most beautiful country."

"I have discovered many countries," said Patrick slowly, as though he could see them before him, one after another, "and this country is very beautiful. But I still have not found the most beautiful country of all, and I wish I could find it at last."

When the shepherd heard this, he jumped up and said, "Patrick, because you have searched tirelessly, I will show you the way."

He took up his staff and walked down the hill to the shores of the lake, and then he drew a circle on the ground with his staff. When he pulled back his staff and took a step back, the earth opened up where he had been standing, and Patrick, who had approached, saw a ladder leading down.

The shepherd said, "If you go down this ladder, you will find the kingdom you are seeking. However you will be in great danger three times. Call my name and I will protect you." The shepherd said good-bye to Patrick and left. Patrick began climbing down the ladder, rung by rung.

He climbed down in the dark until he reached the bottom. Then a path led straight forwards, and he realized that he had arrived in an underground kingdom. After a while, he glimpsed a light in the distance and walked towards it. All around him he could see trees and bushes, and suddenly he stood still, because a lion sprang out at him from the bushes with a tremendous leap, and opened its jaws and roared. When he turned round to escape, he found himself facing a huge wolf, and then when he looked all around, he saw that there were other wild beasts coming at him from the bushes on every side. They opened their jaws to tear him to pieces.

When they had come up to him he remembered the shepherd's advice just in time, and called out, "Good shepherd, help me!"

At that moment, the roaring and howling of the animals stopped. They disappeared as suddenly as they had come, and Patrick was able to go on his way.

The light he had seen became brighter. At last, he climbed up to a place where he could hear sounds of drilling, hammering, and saw-ing. There were huge machines making a tremendous noise, and thin crooked figures in black suits, running to and fro. In the middle there was a gigantic oven, and when Patrick approached it, the figures ran up to him, seized him and dragged him over to the oven. They opened the iron door and threw him into the heart of the fire.

The flames burned him and he shrank with pain and could not utter a word, but in his heart he said, "Good shepherd, help me!" And he saw that the shepherd understood the language of the heart, because the fire was immediately extinguished, the sounds of rattling and thumping stopped, and he was able to go on as if nothing had happened.

This time a path led up to a high and rocky shore. In the depths there was a tumultuous river, but on the other side of the chasm he saw the sun shining in a clear sky. He knew that this was the promised land, and so he went up to the banks and saw that there was a bridge across the river. But what a bridge! It did not have any railing and was very narrow: when Patrick put his foot on it, he slipped because it was as smooth as ice.

Again he said, "Good shepherd, help me!" and at that moment he felt secure. But he had to call on the shepherd at every step, and in that way he crossed to the other side step by step.

Then he fell into a deep sleep, absolutely exhausted. When he woke up, he saw that he had arrived in a shining meadow strewn with flowers which glistened like stars. Two men in white garments approached him and took him by the hand. They led him to a city which glowed with gold, gems and pearls.

When he arrived at the city gates he found his leader, the shepherd, waiting. "This is the country I told you of," he said. "It is paradise. There is no more beautiful country. Because you are brave and did not forget my name, you were able to reach it. You may stay here for a while. Then I'll take you back to the place where you started your journey without any danger. When your life on earth has come to an end you can come and live here forever."

# Thomas

## Where is the palace?

In the days that the twelve Apostles were sent out over the world, Jesus also went to Thomas. He said to him: "Thomas, I am giving every apostle his own task to fulfil. Your task is to go to the east, to India."

"But Lord," answered Thomas, "India is very far away and dangerous. Why are you sending me there?"

"The king is looking for a master builder. He wants to have the most beautiful palace in the world built for him. Only you, Thomas, will be able to do this. You will build this building in my name."

As soon as Jesus had said this, he took Thomas to the market, and it wasn't long before the Indian courtier Abbanes appeared before him dressed in beautiful silk garments.

When he looked round the market, Jesus went up to him and asked him what he was looking for. Abbanes said: "I am looking for a skilled master builder who can build a new palace for my king."

Jesus pointed to Thomas and said, "Abbanes, this is the best master builder I know. You can trust him. No one could build a better castle for you than he."

So Thomas was taken on and went to India with the courtier. The king received him and commissioned him to build the palace. To do this, he gave Thomas a huge treasure and then left for another country for two years.

"When I come back, it must be ready," were his last words.

When the king left the country, Thomas travelled through his entire kingdom. Wherever he went, he divided the treasure amongst the poor. They came up to him in large crowds, not only for the gold and silver, but also to hear the words that Thomas spoke. Wherever he went, he told the story of God's Son coming to earth, and how He had died and had risen from the dead, and how He now wished to build His home in the hearts of men.

After two years, the king returned. He summoned Thomas to him and said: "I commissioned you to build the most beautiful palace in the world. Where is it? Show it to me!"

Thomas answered: "My king, your eyes cannot yet see it. I have built your palace in heaven. It stands there in its full splendour and glory."

The king, who could not understand this, was very angry, and asked: "And what did you do with the treasure which I gave you for its construction?"

"O king, I gave the treasure to the poor," said Thomas. "You will find your true treasure in heaven when you pass through the gates of heaven after this life."

The king felt betrayed by Thomas. He did not know that the most beautiful dwellings are not built on earth, but in heaven. He was furious, and ordered Thomas to be put in chains and thrown into prison. Within a week he was to be executed.

At this time the king's brother was so ill that he died. He went up to heaven and was permitted to choose where he wished to live. Full of admiration, he walked round and pointed out the most beautiful building he saw — a splendid house, decorated with gold, silver and gems.

The inhabitants of heaven told him that this palace belonged to his brother, the king. He had had it built by Thomas, but he did not want it. "If you can go back to earth once more, you can buy it from him," they said.

The king's brother asked whether he might return to earth, and he did so.

When he returned to life, he went down to the prison and opened the doors. He removed the shackles from Thomas's hands and led him outside.

The messengers who had saw this, quickly ran to the king and said: "Lord, king, your brother is alive again and has freed Thomas from the prison. They are coming to see you."

Thus the king received his brother, full of amazement, and his brother said: "Oh king, isn't it amazing that I, your brother, who have just died, am now standing before you, alive? After I died, I was taken to heaven and I saw the most beautiful dwellings there, but the most beautiful of all, my king, is the palace that was built there for you by Thomas. I was permitted to return to you from heaven to tell you this because I would like to buy this palace from you, and I have heard you do not want it."

But the king answered: "My brother, be grateful that you have returned to earth to tell me this. Now that I have heard that the palace of my master builder really exists and is very beautiful, I would like to ask you to have your own palace built by Thomas there, because the one which has been built is mine. And if he does not do so, then there will be room enough in my palace for both of us. But from now on, let Thomas be the first master builder in my court, and he must tell us who taught him his art."

This is how Thomas was restored to his position by the king, and everything he said was written down in books, so everyone who wanted to know could read about it.

# Gregory the Great

## At last he agreed

A terrible plague raged in the great city of Rome. There was a man who lived in that city called Gregory. He tended to the sick day and night; he looked after them and nursed them. At night, he watched over them and prayed for the sick. He prayed above all for the pestilence to pass. Before it finally came to an end, the Pope in Rome, Pelagius, had also died. The people went into the streets and cried: "Gregory must be our new Pope."

However, Gregory quickly went outside and begged the people to choose someone else, because he did not consider himself worthy. No one wanted to listen to him, and so he walked to the city gates and tried to flee from Rome. But the guards at the city gates had been ordered not to let him through, and so, sadly, he went back to his house. The other gates were also guarded day and night, and he was unable to leave the city.

As he still thought that he was unworthy, he took off his fine clothes and dressed as a poor merchant. He went to other merchants who were about to leave the city, and persuaded them to take him with them. They had a horse and cart full of large empty barrels. He crawled into one of them, and in this way, Gregory left the city with the merchants, unnoticed by anyone. They took him to a wood in the vicinity, where he hid in a deep cave.

The people in Rome could no longer find him in the city, and had started to search for him in the surrounding countryside. Suddenly they saw a powerful pillar of light rising up to heaven from the middle of the dark woods. Angels were coming down the pillar of light and going up again.

Filled with awe, those searching went towards the pillar of light, and there discovered Gregory's hiding place. When they told him that he had been found because the angels were carrying the light down to his hiding place and bringing more and more light from heaven to him, he understood how the angels would help him in his difficult task, and at last he agreed to become the new Pope and Bishop of Rome.

# Beatrice

## Had she not gone away?

A long way from the big city and the busy road, there was a convent surrounded by a few small villages and farms. The fields and
meadows stretched into the distance all around. It was very quiet in
this part of the country and the people did not talk much, but from
time to time, the bells of the convent tower rang in the silence, calling
the nuns to their work. Then the people would say: "Listen, that's
Beatrice the sacristan ringing the bell of the convent." Everybody
knew Beatrice. Not only did she always ring the bell of the convent
on time, but she also cleaned the halls, rooms and passageways all
day long. Every morning she opened the doors, and in the evening
she shut them. In this way she helped the women in the convent, but
above all she served Mother Mary, to whom the convent was dedicated. Beatrice truly loved Mary and performed her work, with joy in
her heart.

However, no matter how much she loved Mary, there was another
love concealed deep in her heart. She constantly thought about the
friend she had known since her time at the village school. She had
known him since the age of twelve, and every time she thought of
him, her heart leapt and began to beat furiously. One day, she picked
up pen and paper, and wrote him a letter to tell him how much she
loved him. She asked him to come to her.

Full of joy, the young man leapt on to his horse and spurred it on
to the convent. Then he tethered his horse to the gate and walked
through the blossoming gardens of the convent, to the courtyard and
to a small barred window. He sat down and bent forward to see the
woman, who had been looking out for him for a long time. They
looked at each other and the young man saw that Beatrice was
beautiful, even more so than when they had played together as
children. They talked, and she told him she could not forget him, and
he said he thought she was beautiful, and that she should be with a
knight like him. Finally, he suggested, "If you like, I'll take you with

me to the city where I live. I'll give you jewels and such ornaments as the wife of a knight should wear."

They sat together for a long time, until Beatrice sighed, "Come back to this garden after eight nights and wait for me under that sweet briar, the rose bush which you can see there, and I'll leave the convent and come with you."

The knight swore that he would be true to her, and left. He rode to the city, bought beautiful clothes and valuable jewels, and at the agreed time he sat under the sweet briar and waited in the dusk.

As darkness fell, Beatrice knelt in the chapel with the other women. After the service she stayed behind on her own and went to the altar where Mary's figure stood and said, "Mary, dearest mother, forgive me for leaving. I want to follow this young man because I love him. I cannot help it, I must go with him."

She took off her outer garments and placed them on the altar. Then she took off her shoes and put them on the floor. She hung up the keys in front of the statue of Mary so that they would be discovered the next morning. Then, dressed in her coarse undergarments, she left the convent and the heavy door closed shut behind her. She found her beloved beneath the sweet briar, and he embraced her and kissed her. Then he lifted her up on to his horse and spurred it on.

When they had travelled some way, they stopped after a bend in the road. He dressed her in soft velvet and shiny satin and placed a string of pearls around her neck. He saw how beautiful she looked and she loved him, even without all the gifts he had given her.

They rode on all night until they caught sight of the city. Beatrice asked the knight to rein in the horse for a moment so that she could look back down the road. Then she sighed and said, "Now the women will find the keys which I hung up in front of the statue of Mary and they will realize that I have gone."

But the young knight said, "Don't think about that any more. Here is the city where we will live together."

Then they rode into the city and lived there together for many years.

They had two children. Every morning Beatrice sang the song which she used to sing every morning in the convent. Every evening she gave thanks for everything people gave her; for the wealthy life she lived, and for all the beautiful and good things around her. She also gave thanks for the love of her husband.

But as the years passed, poverty came to the land. The knight brought less and less home to live on, and Beatrice and the children barely had enough to eat. She repaired and patched old clothes until they were completely worn out. The poverty which prevailed made many people bitter. A feeling of discontent and resentment also entered the hearts of Beatrice and her husband, and they often exchanged harsh words. The knight left home for longer and longer periods, and finally he no longer came back at all.

But Beatrice had to look after herself and her sons, and she took hard and heavy jobs in the city so that they would not starve. But every evening when she came home, she washed herself and her clothes, and every morning she still sang the song she had learned in the convent and hoped that Mary would not forget her.

Finally, fourteen years after leaving the convent, Beatrice and her children had to leave her home and were reduced to begging in the streets. They wandered from village to village, and finally came to the region where Beatrice's convent was.

They found shelter with a friendly widow in a house in the neighbourhood. They were given good food and a place to sleep for a few nights. As they were seated at the table, Beatrice suddenly heard the sound of a bell ringing. It sounded as it had always sounded, and she asked the widow about the convent. The good woman answered that there were no better or more faithful people anywhere than the women who lived there. Beatrice said, "But was there not one who was unfaithful and who walked away, fourteen years ago?"

"How can you say that," the widow replied reproachfully. "No one has ever run away from that convent. It is very unkind to talk about our women in that way."

That night Beatrice had a dream. She heard a voice talking to her. "You have wandered long enough and you have suffered great sorrow and deprivation. Come back to the convent. Mother Mary is waiting for you, and the door is open for you."

But the next morning Beatrice thought that the voice that had spoken to her had merely been a dream, and she could not believe in it, not even when she heard it again the next night, speaking the same words. However, on the third night she decided to remain awake and see if the voice would speak to her again.

And indeed, before midnight, she heard the voice for the third time, urging her even more strongly and saying that Mary was calling her to go back. The voice also said, "You should not worry about your children. They will be well looked after, and don't worry that the women in the convent have missed you. While you were away, Mary did your work. No one ever noticed that you had gone."

Beatrice stood up, full of astonishment, and got ready. She kissed her sleeping children and left the hospitable house of the widow. When she came to the convent she found the door open as she had been told, and she went inside. Then she walked through the passageways and was surprised to find that nothing had changed.

When she came to Mary's alcove she saw her garments lying on the altar and her shoes lying on the floor. She put on her garments and shoes and picked up the keys, which were hanging in front of the statue of Mary, exactly as she had left them. She locked the door through which she had come in, and went to her room, where everything was the same as it had always been.

The next morning she rang the bell and the women greeted her as though she had always been there. No one was surprised. Had she been gone at all? Had she dreamt it all? But when she stood before the statue of Mary, she knew that the voice that she had heard the third night had been speaking the truth. Mary had removed her garments from the altar, had worn her shoes and had done her work. It was Mary who had opened and shut the doors every morning and every evening for fourteen years.

And Beatrice looked up at the statue and said, "All those years that I was away you took on my task. Now I have returned. Thank you, Mother Mary."

# Emma

## Take what you can carry

A cruel knight once lived in the castle of Haarlem. He ruled over the surrounding villages with an iron fist, and was feared for his violent nature and brutal behaviour. When he rode out to his estates, everyone bowed down before him in humble greeting as he passed, or all too quickly his hand would reach for his whip, or even his sword.

For a long time the people tolerated the injustice of their lord until their anger erupted and the young and old stood up together as one, and marched to the castle. The fortress was completely surrounded and the people resolved not to surrender until the tyrant had been vanquished. The cruel brute watched helplessly and realised that all his strength was useless against this superior strength, and that he was unable to get any help.

After a while his food supply was used up, and his men were tortured by thirst and weakened with hunger. When he appeared on the battlements himself, the peasants raised their fists at him and shouted out their anger, while boys threw stones at him. Then his fist would tighten around his sword but he would still have to retreat, pale and grim-faced.

However, sometimes the lady of the castle, Emma, would go outside. Then the besiegers would fall silent. They greeted her because they liked her. She had always been kind and good to them. She would look out across the moat at the hundreds of men surrounding the fortress, waiting for the knight to surrender. Emma stood there, an upright figure in her white robes. There was no hatred in her heart for the villagers. She was all too aware of the injustice which the people had suffered, the humiliation and the extortion. She loved her desperate people. But when she turned round and went back into the castle to her husband, she did not feel angry with him either. She knew his wild and restless nature. She was filled with a holy love which illuminated everything around her like the sun.

Finally, the day came that the knight had to bow down his proud head. He called the inhabitants of the fortress together and said, "Dear ladies, brave men. Our food is gone and there is no one outside who will help us. We must surrender because there is no defence against hunger."

When he had finished speaking and looked round the circle, Emma stepped forward and asked if she could talk to the people. She was permitted to do this, and the servants opened the heavy doors and dropped the drawbridge. Then Emma approached the leader, bowed her head and said, "Leader, we have come to this. The fortress will surrender, but allow me to ask you one question."

"Speak, noblewoman," answered the leader.

Emma said, "You have won your fight against our men. Their lives are in your hands, but what will happen to the women of the castle?"

The leader answered curtly, "You did not hurt us at in any way. You may leave the fortress."

"Thank you," said Emma. She smiled, and then added, "Must we leave our possessions behind in the fortress?"

"Take what you can carry," he answered.

Emma looked at him and asked with great emphasis, "Will you permit every woman to carry out the most valuable thing she possesses?"

The leader nodded. "On your word, leader?" asked Emma.

"On my word, noblewoman," answered the leader, and he gestured to her that she could pass this message to the inhabitants of the castle.

Emma again bowed her head to thank him, and then turned round. Back in the fortress she saw everyone in turn, and told the women to collect their most valuable goods. Then she turned to her husband and said, "I may take the most valuable thing I possess out with me, so you'd better make yourself as light as you can."

Thus the women left the castle in a long line, each carrying her own possessions. At the front, Emma tottered under a heavy burden. In her arms she carried the knight, because he was her most valuable possession. She walked between the serried ranks of the people. They stood there silently, staring fiercely at the tyrant they hated. But no one intervened. They let him go because of the woman they loved, and because their leader had given his word.

The fortress was stormed, set alight and razed to the ground. No stone remained unturned, but the knight himself had been saved.

# Agnes

## For you I will go through fire

Egge, the son of the town judge, stood by an old gnarled oak tree, hiding behind its rough trunk. He waited for the girl who passed by everyday. He could think of nothing but her beautiful figure and her sweet face. He wanted to marry her.

The girl, Agnes, came out of school and left the town along the path past the old oak tree which led to her home. She did not know that she was being spied on, but when Egge unexpectedly jumped from behind the oak tree and roughly barred her way, she asked him in astonishment, "Who are you? What do you want?"

"Agnes," said Egge, "I am the son of the judge of this town, and I am very rich. You are the most beautiful girl I know. I love you, and I want you to be my wife."

For a moment it was as though Agnes did not hear him, and as though she was looking past him. Then she turned to him and said softly, "Don't you know that I am the bride of the richest bridegroom on earth?"

The young man stepped back and cried out in disbelief, "No one is richer than me. With my treasures you can buy anything you want."

"You're wrong," said Agnes. "My bridegroom gave me gifts from His riches which you could never give."

"No one could own more than my father and I," shouted Egge. "Show me what he has given you!"

"There are five treasures," answered Agnes. "This ring on my right hand shows that I belong to Him, and that you have no right to me. I wear the necklace of red stones because I love Him so much that I would dare to go through fire for Him. My cloak is stitched with gold thread and protects me against all evil. He placed the belt around my waist and said: 'When you wear this, you will be able to endure anything.' And there is an everlasting treasure waiting for me when He takes me to His kingdom."

When she had said this she turned away and went home.

The young man shouted out with rage. He ran back to the town, ran through the streets to his house, where he shut himself up in his room. Then he fell down on to his bed and wept tears of impotent rage.

His parents heard him and feared that in his sorrow he would harm himself. They asked him why he was crying. He told them what had happened, and then cried out, "I can't bear it to think that she's the bride of another man! She must be mine!"

His father, the judge, made inquiries to find out who the bridegroom could be. He heard that it was Christ. As he did not know Christ, and wished to help his son, he had Agnes brought before him.

When he saw her, he was surprised she was still so young, almost a child. At first he spoke to her kindly and tried to convince her to marry his son. However, when she continued to refuse, he became angry and started to threaten her. However, Agnes looked past him at the window where the sunlight was coming in and shining on her face. The sunlight made the ring on her finger and the stones in her necklace sparkle, and it made her cloak and belt shine.

The judge had to turn his eyes away from her, and felt that he had no power over her. In fear and rage he called out, "If you will not obey, then fire will force you to!"

He ordered his servants to build a wood pile in the square in front of the court of justice. As they were piling up the wood, the people in the town flocked to the square and crowded round the fire. When the fire was lit, the flames leapt higher and higher and the people retreated because of the heat.

But Agnes herself remained standing where she was, right next to the stake. Her hands stroked the red gems of her necklace, which shone like never before.

"For you," she whispered, "and to you I will go through the fire." She did not hesitate and walked forward.

As soon as she had placed her foot on one of the large blocks of wood, the people pointed out a knight standing next to her. His robe shone with light more brightly than the sun. He wrapped her in His red cloak, His right hand stretched out to the flames, which separated, leaving a path free through the middle. The knight followed with Agnes next to Him, protected by His cloak, until they were high up above the people. In a voice which rang out loudly above the crackling fire, He called out, "I will help anyone who loves me. I will save from the fire anyone who is faithful to me, and anyone who is my bride will be with me always."

He led her through the flames away from the town and away from that country, to the place where she would live with Him forever.

# Francis of Paola

## This is my fire

In the town of Paola in the south of Italy, Jacob lived with his wife, Vienna. Although they loved each other very much, their happiness was not complete because after many years together they still did not have a child.

One day as Vienna sat by her window she said, "I suppose we will not have a child any more, we have waited so long." But when she said this, she saw a man in a long brown habit approaching across the street. He walked straight up to their house and knocked at the door. Vienna stood up and unbolted the door.

"What do you want?" she asked the man. "Are you hungry or thirsty, or are you looking for the way?"

"I don't want anything from you," answered the visitor, "I just want to tell you something. I am Francis and I come from Assisi, and because I know the hearts of people I know that you are longing for a child. I have asked God if He will give you a child, and He answered that you will have a son. He will love the earth and the earth will love him. Fire will not harm him and he will not sink in water, while the caves in the rocks will be his dwelling place. However, remember that his love will be so strong that he will leave you very soon for the fire, water and stony earth."

Vienna was so full of joy to hear the words of the pilgrim that she wept, and when she had wiped the tears from her eyes, he had disappeared.

Less than a year later she bore a son and named him after the pilgrim Francis. When the boy grew up, he would spend hours alone sitting by the sea, and when he came home, he would bring back kindling to light a fire. Then he would sit and stare deeply into the flames.

He was only fifteen years old when he went to his parents and said, "Mother and father, thank you for everything you have done for me. I cannot stay with you any longer. I feel that I want to live in the mountains and by the water."

He kissed them farewell, and before he left he asked if he could take some fire.

His father hesitated. "You know that you should not light any fires in the woods. There could be a forest fire. It's forbidden."

"It's my fire," he answered brusquely. "Who can forbid me from doing this? I'll make sure it doesn't do any harm. Have I ever set fire to your house?"

He picked up a few glowing embers in a pot; that was all he required. As he went on his way, he blew on them until they glowed. Up in the mountains he came to a flat meadow in front of a cliff, where he found a cave big enough to live in. He collected stones at the entrance to the cave and arranged them in a circle. Within this circle he scattered the embers, and then placed dry grass and wood on top which soon caught fire.

From that day Francis lived in the cave and his fire always burned there. The thin plume of smoke rose up and dissolved in the deep blue sky. Birds circled above and then landed by him. Small and large creatures were attracted by it because they felt safe and they did not harm each other.

Occasionally, a traveller would pass by. He would also sit down, be given food and drink and then move on. Down in the village the people told each other about the son of Jacob and Vienna who lived up there in the cave and that anyone who wanted to, could go there to warm up at any time of day or in any season of the year.

However, when the sheriff heard about this, he complained that open fires were forbidden, and when the plume of grey smoke continued to rise up and Francis clearly continued to disobey, the sheriff became angry and climbed up to the cave with a soldier. When he entered the meadow, he saw the birds on the branches at the edge of the wood. There was a squirrel on an overhanging branch close by, and a deer lying next to Francis on the ground.

The sheriff came to a halt. "There's the fire," said the soldier, pointing rather uncertainly with his hand. The flames crackled quietly within the stone surround and Francis beckoned the men to approach. He gave them water and fruit and when they had quenched their thirst and eaten their fill, Francis asked them what they wanted.

"Making fires is forbidden," said the sheriff. "Why do you do it?"

"Brother," said Francis, "what is holier than fire? It gives animals its warmth, and all the wood which is rotten and is lying around burns up into pure ash."

When Francis saw that the sheriff was listening, he continued, "Everything on earth is created from light. When it has completed its task it is thrown on to the fire and rises up with the flames back to the light. Everything on earth is a gift from God. With fire we give it back to Him."

"Francis," said the sheriff, "that is certainly true and proper, but I am the sheriff, and I must make sure there are no fires here. Your fire is dangerous. It could get out of hand and spread."

"This fire spread?" said Francis astonished. Then he carefully shook the dust off his hands to clean them and picked up the glowing embers in both his hands to show them to the sheriff. The latter jumped up and backed away in fear, but he also admired Francis when he saw how he held the fire. Then Francis said, "Sheriff, this is my fire. It is meant to warm, not to burn. It is a sacrificial fire, not a destructive fire. Go and tell the people this."

Then he replaced the fire, and the sheriff, who saw that his hands were clean and unharmed bowed deeply before him, and left. After that, no one ever forbade Francis to have the fire and the people talked about him as a saint.

## Francis and the captain

However, Francis was not alone for very long. People kept coming to see him and many wanted to live with him. All the monks who lived there had the power to help people and cure them from their diseases. They also had to travel to distant places very often because people asked them to come in times of sickness and need.

Once he was asked to cross the Straits of Messina to Sicily, where they were expected. Francis left with another monk. Finally, he arrived at the sea and asked a fisherman who was preparing his ship if he could sail across with him. The man looked at him and quickly saw that he would not be earning anything from these people.

"We don't take layabouts," said the fisherman. "We are honest seamen," and he sailed away.

Then Francis knelt down and bowed his head, After a while he stood up again, looked at his fellow monk and said, "God asked us to go to Sicily. He will give us a vessel. Will you give me your cloak?"

The monk was pleased to give him his old worn cloak, and Francis spread it out on the water like a boat. Then Francis went on board as though it was a proud ship. He placed his staff in the middle as the mast and then tied his own cloak to it which immediately billowed out in the wind to form a sail, and thus the two men sailed over the sea towards Sicily.

Meanwhile, at sea the fishermen were casting their nets. One of them looked out over the water as he was working and saw the two monks he had left on the shore, sailing towards them over the waves at great speed.

"Skipper!," he called out, "these are not layabouts, they are holy men."

The captain blushed and gestured to his men. They bowed deeply, cap-in-hand, and beckoned to the monks to come alongside. Then he helped them to board his large fishing boat, and so they were taken to Sicily by the skipper after all.

The people who came to know Francis saw his love of fire and water. They also recognised the love that fire and water had for him and they saw that the caves in the mountains had provided him with a cool place in the daytime and gave protection at night. They said, "He loves the earth and the earth loves him."

# Boniface

## A house was built from the oak tree

In the kingdom of Wessex, a young boy called Winfrith grew up. Once he was travelling along and there was such a terrible storm with such heavy rain that the boy had to shelter in a cave by the side of the road. When he walked in, he noticed that the chasm ended in a stone corridor. He walked down this passage step by step until he came into a larger vaulted cave where he could sit down to wait for the thunder to pass. He had gone in so far that he could no longer hear the rain or the rolling of the thunder. He wondered where he was.

"You are with me," he heard. Then he looked up and saw a man standing there in a long shining robe.

"You have always been with me," the man continued, "but today you will see me and then you will not see me for a long time."

"Will you be leaving me soon?" asked Winfrith.

"That is up to you. I will be travelling through many lands."

"I would like to go with you," said Winfrith.

"I never stay long in one place," the man went on.

"That does not deter me," the boy said.

"Good," answered the man, and looked at Winfrith kindly. "You do not seem to be afraid of long journeys. But before you can come with me, you will have to learn a great deal in the next few years. You must learn to understand the language of the wind and the water, and when you have learned both, call me and I will teach you a new language — the language of silence."

Years passed before Winfrith returned to the cave. He was now an adult, and he said to his angel, "I have learned to understand the language of wind and water, like many people in this land. Now teach me the new language, the unknown language. You called it the language of silence."

"Yes," said the angel, who stood before him again as he had stood many years ago. "I will be pleased to do so."

Winfrith looked up at him and saw that his robe shone as before, but that his face was full of joy, because Winfrith wished to learn new things which very few people know.

In the cave Winfrith learned to understand what becomes audible in silence; he learned to express the things which are in his own heart.

One day, after many years, the angel said, "The language which you have learned now is not an ordinary language. It is a powerful language. It drives out all cares and fear. It is stronger than the voice of the wind and the water. It gives you the strength to speak the truth to the people and to do what is right. And as my servant, you will also be given a new name. Winfrith was the name your parents gave you. From now on you will be called Boniface, he who does the right thing, because anyone who understands the voice that is spoken by the heart can help the people. Now you are ready for the journey. I waited for you. It is time. Follow me as far as you can."

Winfrith, who was now called Boniface, prepared himself and travelled to the east. He sailed across the sea which divides Britain from Friesland and Holland and travelled up the great rivers to Germany. There he crossed mountains and his path led through huge forests until he came to a place called Fritzlar.

In that place there was a mighty ancient oak tree on a hill surrounded by villages and farms. The branches grew in every direction from the powerful trunk. They stretched high up into the air and hung right down to the ground.

When Boniface arrived, many villagers had collected together. They were dancing around the tree, shouting and singing for hours on end. "Donar! Donar! Speak to us," they called out until they were hoarse, and finally fell down utterly exhausted.

Boniface approached them with a huge axe in his hand and said, "Don't you realize that your god is not answering. Look up. He left with the clouds which are passing and disappearing in the distance. He is no longer here. You are calling him in vain."

"You're lying," cried the people, and the men raised their fists and ran towards him. "Our god is still here. His strength can be heard in the rolling thunder. Who are you that you dare to say that he is no longer here?"

"My name is Boniface, and I serve another whose voice can only be heard when the ancient gods have fallen silent. You saw yourself that Donar no longer answers you. Christ wishes to speak to you. Therefore I will cut down your oak tree with this axe, and with the wood I will build a house where his voice can be heard."

The people cried: "Don't you dare to raise your axe against Donar's oak tree. He will strike you down with his terrible lightning."

When Boniface walked up to the tree, unafraid and raised the axe to cut it down, they all jumped up and fled in every direction and looked on fearfully from a distance to see what would happen. The axe fell heavily at the base of the trunk. After a single stroke the tree shuddered from top to bottom. Then it tottered and fell to the ground with a dull thud. Frightened, everyone stared at the tree which had been cut down with a single stroke by this stranger. The birds fluttered up from the felled tree, but nothing else happened. No lightning struck to punish the stranger.

The stranger worked on undisturbed. He cut off the huge branches and split the trunk. Then he made planks and beams from the strong hard wood. The people returned angrily to their homes, but the next day, one or two came to help Boniface, and others followed. A large area was cleared in the woods and the chapel was built there. They built the four walls and left spaces for the tall narrow windows. Then they put on the roof with its heavy joists and broad planks, and all the cracks and holes were filled with mud. Finally, the great wooden door was put into place so that the chapel could open and shut.

From that time the people came together there. When the door closed behind them, it was as quiet as it had once been in the cave where Boniface had learned the language of silence. In this language he now spoke about Christ, who came to the people when the ancient gods left. "Let Christ live in your hearts," said Boniface, "then he will also live in this house when you have gathered here together. In this house that we built from the wood of Donar's oak tree."

Although Boniface had to travel to many lands, he always returned to Fritzlar. He grew old, but still stood up straight, though his hair had turned a shiny, silvery-white and grew down to his shoulders. The people loved him because he was good to them. One morning he went to the chapel earlier than usual. It was so early that the sun had not yet risen, and yet the space was suddenly lit up and Boniface saw that his angel was standing in front of him.

"My friend," said the angel, "you followed me on many journeys and you never lagged behind. Today I am calling you for the last time. Follow me now to the west, to the country of Friesland by the sea. This is the last place where you will work. And when the end comes, do not be afraid, for I will be there always, and the greater the danger, the closer I will be to you."

Boniface bade farewell and left Fritzlar with a number of monks.

He travelled over the same mountains and through the same forests which he had crossed before.

He entered Friesland with joy in his heart to teach the people there the new language. The men pitched their tents in the town of Dokkum and many people came to them, wanting to hear what Boniface had to say.

One morning, they got up early to get everything ready for the guests they were expecting that day. They were sitting in their tents when Boniface said to one of his brothers, "I can hear someone calling. Should I go?"

His friend listened and said, "I hear many voices. They are shouting and threatening, as though they wish to hurt us."

"No," said Boniface, "I can hear the voice clearly now. It is calling to say that my time has come and that I should go."

"But look!" his friend called, frightened, and he pointed outside where a group of wild men were running into tents carrying clubs and axes.

These men, who hoped to steal money and treasure from the travelling strangers, broke into the tents. In their greed for valuable booty, they ripped open everything they saw and destroyed everything in their way.

One of them rushed into Boniface's tent and dragged him out. However, his axe fell on the huge book of the Gospels which Boniface had written himself, and which he was holding in his hand, cutting through the spine and the pages.

Then the robber struck out again and hit Boniface himself.

When the old man fell down the robber retreated from the tent. Did he see the angel who picked up his true servant in his arms and took him to his kingdom? The pillage continued, but the savage looters found little booty, and a fight broke out for the little they did find. The robbers fought each other, and only a few of them survived. They were punished severely.

However, the book was found and has survived up to the present day. The people who found it saw the deep cut through the pages. However, when they started to read the book they realized that the stroke had not passed through a single word or even a single letter. Everything that Boniface had written remained untouched.

# Paschal Baylon

## And the water always welled up

When the bells of the small village church started to ring out on the morning of Easter, a child was born in a hut on the edge of the village. It was a boy and his parents named him Paschal, after the Spanish word for Eastertide.

There was little other than a box and a coarsely woven cloth to put him in, but it seemed to be enough for him because he was always happy and contented. As soon as he could walk, his father, who was a shepherd, took him with him to his flock of sheep. He learned to herd the sheep and look after them, and as time went by, he became a shepherd himself. When his father saw that he was old enough, he gave him part of his herd.

However, before going off by himself without help, Paschal went to the woods. He knew there was a large tree in a clearing. There he found a strong, straight branch and cut it to make himself a shepherd's crook. From that moment he always had his crook with him. He leant on it when he was tired. He jumped across ditches with it or pushed back branches of the undergrowth when one of his flock became entangled. However, no one had ever seen him striking anyone or any creature with his crook.

Spain is country where the sun shines fiercely, especially during the long summer days when it is so hot and dry that you often have to look for water. The people carefully keep the water they carry with them, and the animals seek the shade and wait with dry throats for the coolness of evening.

Paschal loved his sheep and dogs. He saw their pleading eyes when the sun burned high up in the sky. Then he did what his heart told him to do, and struck the earth with his crook. The curious thing was that every time he did this, water would well up from the ground in that place so that the animals could quench their thirst at the spring.

One day, Paschal met another group of shepherds with their

flocks. They looked tired and downcast and complained that they had nothing to drink. Paschal was surprised, and asked them why they did not strike the ground with their crooks so that water would appear. The shepherds stared at him in astonishment, but tried it anyway. However, no matter how much they beat their crooks on the ground they produced only dust and grit and there was no water.

Paschal did not understand this at all; it had never happened to him. He raised up his own crook, struck it on the ground and behold, the water welled up in a clear spring and the shepherds and animals could drink as much as they wanted.

The shepherds looked at each other, shaking their heads. "Of course, he knew all along that there was water in the ground beneath his feet. That's why he stood there. Come, we will take him to the barren plains where nothing can grow because it is too dry. Let's see what he can do there."

However, when they had climbed up the steep hill with him and had arrived at the rockiest part, the water also bubbled up there as soon as Paschal's crook touched the ground. After that, the people in the area looked up to him shyly, respectfully and also rather enviously. They noticed that Paschal's animals always had enough to drink, and were very surprised when they heard how he did this.

One day a monk walked up to him and asked him whether he would not like to come and live with them and become a priest.

"I would like to help you in your monastery," he said. "But let me be the porter. I am not learned enough to be a priest. The priest must stand at the altar; let me work with my crook." Then he added, "After all, I can't simply abandon my flock."

And in this way Paschal, who was already a shepherd, also became a porter and everybody was satisfied.

He did not grow very old. When he was fifty-two, he felt himself becoming weaker and weaker and his friends saw that he would not live much longer.

That year, when the bells of the small village church started to ring out on the morning of Pentecost, he looked up at the people standing around him, and he said, "My friends, this is the day on which I was born. Today I will also leave you. May all be well with you, and when you place my body in the earth, put my crook in my right hand; I would like to have it with me wherever I go."

# Veronica

## You don't have to go to the painter

Tiberius, the Emperor in Rome, was ill. Many doctors had tried to cure him, but he remained weak and the pain would not subside. When even the last doctor had not been able to help him, Tiberius called out in desperation, "Is there really no one who can cure me?".

The doctor answered, "Emperor, there is one physician who could still help you. However, he lives far away from here, in the country of Palestine. He is Jesus of Nazareth. He can cure anyone who wishes to be healthy."

The Emperor thanked the doctor, called his counsellor Volusianus, and sent him to Pontius Pilate, the governor of Palestine, to ask him where this Jesus was to be found. "Bring him to me, because I would like to be cured," he said.

Volusianus sailed to Palestine and travelled to Jerusalem, where he asked Pilate whether he knew this miraculous doctor, and where he was to be found. Pilate was afraid when he heard this. He knew the name of Jesus well. Jesus of Nazareth had died, not long before. Pilate might have been able to save him from death but he hadn't done so. Now the Emperor would certainly punish him when he heard what had happened. He tried to hide his fear from the counsellor and said, "Volusianus, I must think about this. Give me a few days to think it over. Make yourself comfortable in my palace. Eat and drink and have a rest from your long journey. I will see if I can find a good doctor for you."

But Volusianus thought about the sick Emperor. He could not rest and started looking himself in the great city of Jerusalem. He came to the great square in front of the temple and because it was hot and he was tired, he sat down on a bench where a peasant woman was sitting.

The woman saw that he was tired. She turned to him and asked, "Lord, you look tired. Can I do anything for you?"

131

"Well," answered the counsellor, "I am not concerned for myself, but for another who is very dear to me."

"Lord," said the woman, "tell me what you are worried about." Then Volusianus told her about the sick Emperor and how he had come to Palestine to find the physician, Jesus of Nazareth. Finally he concluded, "I have the feeling that I will not find him, and what is to happen to our poor Emperor then?"

Veronica, for this was the woman's name, bent down to him and said, "Lord, perhaps I can help you. But first I must tell you that Jesus recently died. You will not find him here any more. Your feeling about this was right."

Volusianus bowed his head and was silent for a long time. Then he suddenly looked up. He looked at Veronica and said, "You said you might be able to help me, anyway."

"Yes, Lord," she answered, "but first I must tell you my story." The important counsellor nodded, to show that he agreed, and Veronica began.

"It must have been two or three years ago that I first met Jesus here in Jerusalem. He spoke to us and cured our friends. He also came to our homes and I looked after him and gave him food and drink. When he was here I was happy, and that happiness freed me from all my sorrow and worries. However, he often went to different places throughout the country. Then my days were long and gloomy, and I thought only about whether he would quickly return. One day, I was standing by my linen cupboard and a cloth fell into my hand, so pure and white that I thought, 'I will take this to the painter at the end of our street. He must paint Jesus's face on this cloth. Then I will hang up the cloth in my room, and I will always be happy.'

"And Lord, I never wait long when I have a good idea, so I stood up and walked to the painter, but before I reached his house, Jesus came towards me on the other side of the street. He greeted me and asked me where I was going. When I showed him the cloth and told him why I was going to see the painter, he indicated that I should give him the linen cloth and I did so.

"Then this hot and tired man, just like you, Lord, took the cloth which had recently been in my cool house and pressed it to his face with both hands. Then he folded the cloth carefully with both hands and gave it to me like a treasure he was entrusting to me.

"'Veronica,' I heard him saying, 'you don't have to go to the painter. Take this cloth home and keep it carefully. In your hands this peace of linen will be able to cure the sick, because this image of me has great power.' And so I did what Jesus told me."

Veronica was quiet for a moment and then she added, "Lord, I already told you that Jesus has died. But I have been able to cure many sick people since his death." The counsellor jumped up. "Woman!" he cried, "Give me this cloth, so that I may cure my Emperor. I will pay you with pieces of gold."

"No, Lord. Jesus said, 'This cloth will only cure the sick in your hands, Veronica.' It's not for sale for any amount of gold."

"Then come with me to Rome quickly! The Emperor is waiting for me." And so she followed Volusianus across the sea to Rome. She kept the piece of linen with her wherever she went. When they came to Tiberius, she stood quietly and seriously by his sick bed. The cloth opened in her hands and the Emperor looked at the face on it. It was a face of wisdom and goodness. This wisdom and goodness restored his health and he became strong again, and the pain disappeared.

Throughout her life, Veronica showed this image to the sick and restored them to health in this way, and the cloth never lost its power.

# Lioba

## Dear red ball of wool, roll!

Michael and his wife Ebba lived in Britain, high up on the steep coast. The surf of the sea pounded against the white chalk cliffs down in the depths below their house.

Michael was a fisherman. Every morning he went down a narrow path to the bay where his boat was moored to sail out to sea. He returned late in the evening with his basket on his back, bent double under the burden of the fish he was carrying. This was his work, day after day.

Michael and Ebba did not have any children, and during the day while her husband was at sea, Ebba would sit at the window and look out over the bobbing grey waves. She would see the sun rise in the east, and when its light shone in the room she would start work in the house and the garden until all the work was done. Then there was a lot of time left over and she would sit by the window and think, "It's quiet around us and empty in the house. Why isn't a child born to us?"

One day, after many years, she realized that she was carrying a child. Not long afterwards, she could feel it moving. Now the hours of the day passed quickly because she had many things to prepare for the birth.

During this time, Ebba had a dream one clear night. She was sitting on the top of the cliff and the sea surged below her. She knew that she was carrying a child and when she looked at her lap, something glistened between the folds of her cloak, like metal. When she opened her cloak, there was a shining bronze bell. She lifted up the bell and shook it gently from side to side until the clapper inside the bell struck the side. The note which sounded was powerful and carried far away across the sea and the land.

When Ebba woke up, she could still hear the note, and when she felt under her heart she could feel the child moving, and thought, "It will not be long before you are born, and later when you grow up, your voice will reach many people, just as the note of this bell sounds far and wide over the world."

The child was a girl and her parents called her Truthgeba, which means "gift of God."

But when the girl grew up, she was so kind to all the people around her that they called her Lioba which means, "she who gives love," and this was the name by which she was known all her life.

Lioba had no brothers or sisters, but she had heard that her mother Ebba's sister's son had once left Britain and had crossed the sea to Holland and had gone from there to Germany. He was called Winfrith, and was later known as Boniface.

She thought about him a great deal when she was a little girl, and the more often she left the house so that she could see far across the sea from high up on the cliff, the more she had to think of him. Once Lioba had an idea, she always had to carry it out. She took a goose quill, dipped it in a pot of black ink and wrote to Boniface to say that she was prepared to go to him if he needed her.

Not long after a messenger had taken the letter, she also had a dream. Like her mother, she was sitting by the sea. In this dream she put her hand to her mouth and took out a purple thread. She took hold of the thread and wound it and wound it until she was holding a large round ball which shone in the light. She saw that she was standing so close to the water that it was washing around her feet. She bent down and placed the ball on an incoming wave, which then rolled back and took the ball with it. She held the end of the thread in her hand and the ball rolled with the wave far, far away into the sea to the east.

When Lioba woke up she did not see a ball and did not feel any water washing around her feet, but she longed to cross the sea and go to her cousin Boniface, because she wanted to help him.

That morning, Boniface's letter arrived and told her that she could come.

"Go straight to the east across the sea," he wrote, "through the low countries, over the mountains and through the forests. I will wait for you in the house I built myself."

She was filled with great joy, and not long afterwards she kissed her father and mother and bade them farewell, saying goodbye to the flowers, the birds and all the countryside around.

"Dear red ball of wool, you rolled away to where my brother is waiting for me," she said softly to herself. "Now I will follow you and I will not rest until I have found him."

The ship which carried her and the feet which led her took her to the strong oak house where she knocked nervously on the door and was warmly welcomed by Boniface.

The house was full of great joy. The monks sang a song of welcome and brought her food and drink. Lioba's arrival was celebrated joyfully. Boniface then showed her the house. He took her to the villages around and to the houses of the people so that she met everyone. However, this did not last very long, because Boniface's angel had already commanded him to travel on to other regions.

When the full moon started to wane and once more appeared in the sky as a small crescent, Boniface went to Lioba and said, "Dear sister, dear friend, my leader tells me that I must travel on. You were prepared to help me. Please be a mother to the people who live around this house. I must go, but my strength will protect you. I do not have any gold or jewels, I can't gave you any money or goods, but take from me this handful of salt. It will protect you from all danger."

Boniface opened his right hand in which he held a little bit of bright white salt. Lioba took a cloth, put the salt in it, tied up the ends together and placed the cloth in her cloak.

"I will always carry the salt with me, Boniface" she answered. "If your strength lies in this salt I need not be afraid of anything."

"There is great strength in it," said Boniface, "the Lord himself becomes strong in us through this salt. Do as you promised and carry it with you always. Never forget."

What happens when a father or mother or a good master leaves? Then evil seizes its chance. One night Lioba was woken up by shouting and moaning which could be heard even in the chapel. Through the high windows she saw the flashing lightning and heard the loud roll of thunder. In her throat she felt the biting smoke of a fire. When she heard the crackling of the fire, she jumped up and quickly ran outside. The night air was red with flames which rose up from the houses and were dangerously close to the chapel. Lioba ran towards the desperate people, and called back those who wanted to flee. "Get water from the river!" she called in a loud voice. "Quickly!"

"What can one scoop of water do to stop this terrible fire?" they called out in desperation, and once again tried to flee.

"Get buckets and fetch water!" called Lioba with a voice that sounded like the bell in her mother's dream.

"Bring the water here."

Some people now took courage. They went to fetch water and

soon came back. One full bucket was soon put down in front of Lioba.

Then she took the folded cloth from her cloak and scattered some salt into the water. "Lord," she prayed, "extinguish this terrible fire." She walked to the fire with the bucket and threw the water into the flames herself.

The wild flames were tamed as though by a mighty hand; they subsided and the glow was extinguished. Then the fire merely smouldered and could be extinguished by the people with water from the river. The chapel was saved and no one had been injured, and the houses were repaired. But from that day the people knew that although Boniface had gone, the strength with which he had protected them was now with Lioba. This power stayed with her even long after her brother had left this earth. For many years she protected the people in this way against fires and storms, against robbers and wild beasts. Lioba carried Boniface's gift with her as a silent secret, and the salt was never finished in all the years that she lived in the wooden house in the forest.

After Lioba died, people often prayed for her protection, and they still do now. Pictures of her always show her with a bell and a flash of lightning. The bell is the bell in the dream of her mother, Ebba, and the lightning is the lightning which could not hurt her.

# Ambrose

## His words are as sweet as honey

Ambrose was a famous bishop of Milan in the north of Italy. Many people came to hear him speak because he explained everything so clearly that the people could understand him very easily. They noticed that they always felt happy when listening to him, and they said to each other, "His words are sweet, as sweet as the honey from the bees."

In fact, his father had predicted this when Ambrose was still a very small child. This is what happened.

One beautiful, sunny day, his father and mother carried him into the garden in his cradle. The cradle stood on the lawn full of flowers and surrounded by blossoming fruit trees. In the trees and on the lawn bees hummed softly as they looked for honey in the flowers.

Then the father and mother, who were sitting in the porch, heard the buzzing grow louder and saw the bees collecting in a large swarm over the middle of the garden and settling on the child in the cradle. They covered not only the cradle, but also the child, and his whole face.

Little Ambrose slept and breathed through his mouth which was half open, and the bees crawled not only all over his eyelids, but also in and out of his mouth.

His father and mother were terribly frightened, but they did not dare go near because they were afraid that the bees would sting the child with their venomous stings. And so they stood on the porch and waited until they heard that the buzzing, which had stopped while the bees were with Ambrose, had started again. Buzzing loudly, the bees finally flew up from the cradle and away from the child. In a large swarm, they flew up higher and higher into the sky until they could no longer be seen.

The parents then quickly walked to Ambrose and could smell the fragrance of the honey over his entire body, but particularly in his mouth where the bees had crawled in and out. And the father said, "It's a miracle that the bees did not harm you, my child, and they left their honey in your mouth. I think that the words you will speak later will be as sweet as the honey that you will taste when you wake up."

BARTHOLOMÄUS ZEITBLOM

# Margaret of Antioch

## Your name means pearl

It was morning. The sun rose above the edge of the wood and shone through the windows of the small wooden hut by the lake. The light fell on a face of a girl who was sleeping by the wall opposite the windows.

"Margaret, wake up," sang the light. "You will be fourteen years old today. Wake up quickly, day is breaking."

You don't have to say that twice to a girl who's having a birthday. She rubbed her eyes, looked around, jumped out of her bed and got dressed. Milk and bread were standing ready for her, as well as a large bowl of flowers and fourteen candles. An older woman with a kind face came in, kissed Margaret, and started to light the candles. Margaret looked at them, and when they were all burning, she said, "Mother Christine, how often have you lit the birthday candles for me? You said I could ask you today."

"Well," said Mother Christine and sat down, "this will be the twelfth time because you came here to me when you were two years old."

"Now that I am fourteen," said Margaret, "will you tell me, as you promised you would, where I came from, and who my mother and father were?"

"Your mother died young, I didn't know her. Then your father brought you to me. He was the patriarch of the city of Antioch. He was an important man, and he asked me to bring you up. So you are of noble lineage and I am merely a simple country woman."

Margaret looked up and said, "Well, at least you have always looked after me, and my father never came to see me again."

"That is true," answered Christine.

"Mother," said Margaret, "you also promised me that from today, I could go out with the flock of sheep on my own. I can hear them bleating already, they want to leave the barn. Can I go?"

"A promise is a promise," said Christine, "but don't forget, in the sun you are safe. In the shadows there is danger. Will you remember?"

And so Margaret went out with the flock of sheep in the direction of the big wood where the sun was still low in the sky, casting long shadows over the fields where the animals were grazing. All day, she looked after them, and when the trees and clouds cast their shadows, she had to lead her sheep towards the light of the sun, because a wolf or a bear might suddenly appear from the woods to seize one of the sheep from the flock.

In the evening the animals drank on the shores of the lake by the hut and then went into the barn in a long row. Margaret shut the door and went to stand by the lake for another moment. Clouds had moved across the sun, which had almost set. A wind rose, blowing over the water so that small waves rippled to the shore.

Then, as though a curtain was drawn aside, the clouds suddenly drifted apart and between their bright golden borders, a long shaft of sunlight shone over the water to the place where Margaret was standing. At the moment that the glittering light seemed to travel towards her, it was as though the earth beneath her feet shook, not violently, but tremblingly as though great something was approaching.

From the clouds, a figure appeared, the figure of a man who came towards her in the shaft of light. His robe was made of immaculate white linen, and the cloak he wore over this glowed a warm red. She saw that where he walked the water became smooth, and when he had come to her, the wind was still.

He stood next to her and stretched his hand over the lake. "Look, Margaret," he said, "can you see the sun descending from heaven to earth. It will not be long before it is there."

They stood side by side. Margaret could not remember later how long this lasted, but when the orange glow touched the earth she turned to him and said, "Who are you?"

"I am your friend," he answered, "and a shepherd of men."

When the sun sank in the water, she asked, "Will you leave me again, or will you stay with me?"

He answered: "Once I came from the sun to the earth. I was crucified there by the people. Since then I have been here. I want to be with you too. So never forget, call me when you are in great danger and I will help you."

The next day when Margaret was in the fields with the sheep again, it was very dark. The clouds hung low above the land. She gazed at the edges of the wood, to see if a wolf or bear might be coming, but they didn't appear. However, a group of horsemen came riding up the road.

When the first horseman, a knight, looked up and saw Margaret, he reined in his horse sharply, gestured to a servant and ordered him to bring the shepherdess to him. When she stood before him, he asked her name, who her father was, and for whom she was working.

"My name is Margaret," she answered, "my father is Theodosius, the Patriarch of Antioch, and Christ is my lord."

The knight kept a strong rein on his restless horse to control it, and said, looking down on her, "You come from a noble family and your name means 'pearl,' which suits your beautiful figure. But how can you follow someone who died on the Cross?"

Margaret, who could hear the scathing tone of his voice, said quietly, "That is what He wanted."

Then the knight called out mockingly, "He didn't defend Himself when they put Him on the Cross. You call that a man? Come with me. I am Olybrius, the richest and most powerful knight. You will be my wife if you forget Him."

Margaret stepped back, looked the knight straight in the eyes and said, "What does your power mean? I belong to Him for whom wild animals are obedient, for whom the wind is still and the water is smooth. Yes, the earth itself shakes for Him."

"If you reject me you will die!" Olybrius cried out furiously," then you will see who is powerful around here."

"I am His bride," answered Margaret.

At a sign from the knight, his servants seized her. One of them placed her in front of him on his horse and the procession quickly rode to Olybrius's fortress. There she was thrown into the dungeon under the fortress. For a long time, she sat there with her back against the wall in the darkness. It was cold and damp in this dungeon and she was trembling with cold, and yet she remembered what had happened that day and the day before. She thought of her birthday and of Mother Christine. She also thought of the man who had come across the water in the evening sun, how the earth had shaken beneath her feet in expectation, and how the waves and the wind had been still. When she thought of these things she felt strength and courage in her heart. She also felt that she wanted to know who was keeping her in prison. So she stood up, took a deep breath and called out, "Who is it? Who has imprisoned me here? My enemy, show me who you are."

When she had called out, the darkness around her turned into an enormous dragon. It came at her out of the corner of the dungeon and opened its mouth to devour her, but Margaret did not feel any fear, and when the darkness enveloped her, she called out, "My shepherd, help me!"

At these words the dragon curled up and broke apart, and then the darkness also fell away. Light streamed in from every side and when she looked up, she saw Christ standing next to her. "You are my bride," He said, "from now on you will live with me in my kingdom."

# Odilia

## Because she had no light in her eyes

Duke Etticho and his wife, Bereswinda, lived in the castle of Hohenstein high up in the mountains. The duchess was sitting by her window one day, pleating the canopy of a cradle that was standing in front of her. Etticho was turned away from her and was looking outside. He could see the land over which he reigned stretching out into the distance. It lay blistering in the sun at the bottom of the steep mountain where the fortress was built.

"I want a son," said the duke, "a son who will succeed me to reign over this land."

"It will not be long," said Bereswinda softly. "Then we will know what God has granted us — a boy or a girl."

"I want a son," said the duke, and he turned around and walked outside with a heavy tread. The door shut behind him.

Less than a month later, Bereswinda's servant went to her lord early in the morning and asked him to come and see his newborn daughter. Etticho saw the beautiful child lying quietly in her mother's arms. He took a deep breath when he saw that it was a girl. He was disappointed, but didn't say anything and soon went back to his own room.

In the following days, the mother and servants played with the child and noticed that she was always looking quietly into the distance without following their movements. In fact, she only noticed the people who came to her if she heard them or if they touched her.

A wise old servant, who had helped many mothers with their children, finally told them that this beautiful child could not see them because she had no light in her eyes, and she was blind.

A blind girl — Duke Etticho was furious when he heard this. He was so angry that he shouted at the mother that he did not wish to keep her at his castle. Yes, the girl would have to be taken away, it did not matter where.

When he became more and more insistent week after week and

more and more furious, poor Bereswinda gave the child to a trusted servant and had her taken far away to the Convent of Palma, where her sister would look after the girl.

Years passed, and during this time Bereswinda had a second child, a son, of whom Etticho was very proud. They called him Hugo and he was to be his father's successor. During this time, their daughter also grew up to become a beautiful girl. All those years she lived in Palma, but still could not come home.

A long way away there was a bishop Erhard, and one night he dreamt that an angel ordered him to go to Palma. There he would find a blind girl and he would baptize her in a spring in a wood.

The angel's words were so powerful that Erhard got ready immediately and started on his journey. It took him fourteen days to make the long trip to Palma. When he arrived, he found the duke's daughter and took her with him to a cave in the wood nearby where there was a spring. He told her to kneel down and sprinkled clear water from the spring over her. He spoke the words of baptism and gave her the name he had heard in the dream.

"I am giving you the name, Odilia," he said, "which means God's sun. May God's sun shine in your heart, and if God permits, also in your eyes." With these words he sprinkled the water on her eyes, which still looked aimlessly into the distance as they had done since birth.

However, when he had spoken these words, and the water had touched her eyes, they shone, and for the first time she could see the world around her. The first person she saw was Erhard. She thanked him with all her heart. Then she went to the other people standing around and embraced them. For the first time in her life, she was happy. Her small world had become light and rich.

When she returned to the monastery, everything seemed too small and too restricted to her and she wished to see her father and mother, as well as the brother she had never met. One day a messenger arrived at Hohenstein with a letter for Hugo and the messenger told him that this letter was meant for him alone.

It was the first letter he had ever received from his sister and when he read it, he was happier than he had ever been. He jumped up, ran to his father and called out from a distance, "Father, father. My sister Odilia writes that she wants to meet me and asks if she may come here to the castle." But Etticho was once again overcome with his former rage and disappointment when he heard this and his answer was a firm "no." Then Hugo left his father shocked and saddened. For many days, he sat by his window which looked over the plains, and grieved.

Then he thought, "My father probably didn't understand. I will ask her myself to come here." And so he sent his servant off with two horses to fetch her. In the following days he sat by the same window looking out, until at last he saw two horsemen coming towards the castle — a man and a woman.

He saw his father behind him, seizing him by the shoulders. He growled, "Who are they, right in front of us coming up here? I'm not expecting any visitors."

"I am," said Hugo. "I'm expecting my servant who is coming here with my sister."

Then Etticho became so furious about Hugo's disobedience and the return of the daughter he had exiled, that he took a stick and hit his son so hard that he had to be taken away by the servant and could not stand up or walk for a long time.

Odilia arrived at Hohenstein and her father was so shocked about what he had done to his son that he let her in and allowed her to stay. She lived there month after month, and the people whispered to each other, in the castle, around the castle, in the villages and throughout the country, that the oldest daughter had returned and that she was now called Odilia, whose eyes had been cured by a miracle. Above all, the people whispered to each other that she was very beautiful, and shouldn't a beautiful woman get married?

Etticho also thought of this, and while Bereswinda was glad that Odilia was with her, Etticho became more and more restless, and insisted that his daughter should accept the offer of one of the knights who wanted her to become his wife, because many came and were constantly rejected by her. "Father" she said every time, "my heart cannot belong to one man. It belongs to many."

Finally, his fury flared up again, and Etticho shouted at her, "You will marry the next knight who asks for your hand, whoever it is. I have waited long enough now."

Then Odilia understood that she must flee, and she did so when the next knight came to Etticho to ask for her hand. All alone, she walked down the mountain that night, across the wide plains and when the sun rose, a ferryman took her across the River Rhine. On the other side she walked on into the mountains. By the time she had got this far, her father had discovered her flight, and together with the knight, he leapt on to his horse and they tore down the mountain across the plain after her.

Finally, as she was climbing slowly up a mountain path, Odilia heard the sound of horses' hooves behind her. She knew that she was being pursued and looked around to see where she could hide, but could not see anywhere. There were only solid rock walls rising up on either side of the road. In despair, she knelt down and prayed, "Lord of earth, help me in my time of need!"

When she looked up, the rock wall opened up in front of her to let her in. The knights who came galloping up on their horses to seize her saw her enter the crevasse, and arrived just as the rock wall closed behind her.

They were extremely frightened and looked at the rock fearfully. They felt the stone and then retreated respectfully. Had the earth itself come to Odilia's aid? Slowly Etticho's rough heart was filled with sorrow for his daughter, and he realised that God Himself must love her if He had restored her sight and protected her from him.

"My daughter!" he called out, "Forgive me. I will help you in future. I will no longer force you to do anything you don't want."

Then the rock opened and Odilia stepped out. When she emerged from the dark, the light shone all around her, and the men saw that she was more beautiful than ever. Etticho placed her in front of him on his horse to ride back, but before they rode away, the rock started foaming. Water appeared from the opening, and flowed down. It continued to flow through the years, and it is said that the blind can be cured at this spring.

When they came home, the duke gave his daughter the big house of Niedermünster at the foot of the mountain. She went to live there and soon her hopes were fulfilled. Poor people, unhappy people, sick and tired people came to her and were welcomed into her home. She helped them, supported them and looked after them. Many of them were able to return to the world after a short while. Some stayed longer, but they all said, "Odilia was always with us, like the sun who warms us to give us new life. She was God's sun who made us strong so that we could live."

# Brendan

## And he looked into the depths

Brendan lived long ago in the country of Ireland and sailed the seas for many years with his comrades. One of the secrets of his life that I want to tell you about, is that he was never afraid.

His foster mother, Ita, who looked after him while he was a small boy discovered why this was. She described how he would sit next to her on the ground in the garden and play. While he played, he often started talking and laughing with someone she couldn't see. Once, when he was laughing loudly and she didn't know why he was having so much fun, she asked him, "Is there anyone else in the room?"

"Yes, of course," he answered, "There are lots more women here. They look like you, but they have much more beautiful clothes than you. They often come to play with me."

Then Ita understood that he was talking to angels and laughing with them, and she also understood why he never had any accidents and why he was never afraid. The angels protected him and he could follow them when they led him along dangerous paths.

Brendan grew to adulthood and left home and built a hut by the sea with many other monks who wished to live and pray quietly, just as he did.

Brendan often sat on his own. He would think about the time when the angels used to come to him, and he sighed because it seemed as though they had abandoned him. He would ask, "Do you live in another kingdom? Are you no longer there? Or can I just not see you any more? Oh, do let me know where you are."

One day as he was thinking these thoughts and asking after the angels, a man came to visit him. He was called Barinthus. He had been away with his boat and Brendan asked him about the things he had seen.

"I was with my son, Merdoc," answered Barinthus.

"And what did you do when you were away?" asked Brendan.

Barinthus was eager to tell him all about it, but warned him that it was a long story. So Brendan took him to his hut and heard the wonderful story, how Barinthus had been taken by Merdoc in the latter's boat, and how they had sailed out to sea and were soon shrouded in a thick fog. They sailed through this until light shone again and an island lay before them, so beautiful that Barinthus talked about it for hours. Then Brendan understood that this was the country where the saints lived as well as the angels, and he listened attentively so that he would not miss any of the story.

While Barinthus was telling this story, other monks joined them and they all sat and listened until, after a long time, Barinthus ended his story by recounting how he had returned home from that island.

In the following days, Brendan couldn't think of anything other than the island. The others couldn't forget the story either, so they decided to build a boat and set sail to find the island.

When the boat was ready and everything had been prepared for the journey, Brendan embarked with fourteen other monks and tried to set sail from the shore. However, they heard voices calling them, and saw three men running up to them. As soon as they got to the boat, they asked urgently whether they could come along on the trip. Brendan knew them and wanted to send them away, but they were so insistent that he finally agreed.

"If that's what you want, despite my warning, I just hope that you don't have an accident."

But they laughed, climbed into the boat and helped to row out to sea.

One of the fourteen monks chosen by Brendan himself asked him whether he thought the trip would be a success, and he answered, "My friend, before I decided to risk this trip, I stood for a long time on the large rock on the coast to ask the king of the elements whether I could make this trip. After a while an angel came to stand next to me and pointed into the distance, over the sea, and then the island which Barinthus told us about appeared. It glowed with light and was surrounded by many angels. I didn't see it for very long, but long enough not to forget it until we reached it.

"The angel said two things to me: 'You will reach your goal,' and 'I will always be by your side. You can trust in me.' Therefore my friend, I think we will succeed in this trip. However, I am greatly concerned about the three men who would not listen to me, but who came with us nevertheless. We must take great care to make sure that no evil befalls them."

They sailed for many weeks. Sometimes they rowed on the calm seas, and sometimes a powerful wind swelled the sails of the boat. At last, after seeing only sea water for a long time, they came to an island. It was high time, because they had finished all the food and drink they had brought with them. However, there were tall cliffs all round the coast and they had to sail right round the island until they found a small harbour, just big enough for the boat to enter. They disembarked and looked for something to eat and drink. They found a narrow path leading upwards. But the path came to a dead end, and they found themselves standing between trees and rock and didn't know how to go on. But then they saw something move. A little dog came running towards them wagging its tail, and then ran into the woods further up the hill. When they followed it, they came to a clearing with a green meadow and a beautiful big house.

Inside, the table was laid, covered with delicious food and drink, and they ate and drank their fill. But on the wall there were very precious horses' reins and bridles, made of leather and worked with gold and silver. When they went to sleep that night, Brendan noticed that one of the men he would have preferred to leave behind kept looking at the reins. Brendan prayed and hoped fervently that the monk would not take what did not belong to him.

However, the next morning when they were all ready to go on, he said, "One of you has taken a golden bridle and is hiding it."

With a cry of fright that he had been discovered, and that he had been tempted by the gold and silver, the monk removed the bridle from under his habit and cast it away. Then he fell down exhausted on to the ground, and Brendan, who was standing next to him, saw that he had no strength left to go on.

"Oh, Father Brendan, forgive me for what I have done," he cried, "and think of me when I am no longer with you, because I know that I cannot live much longer."

The monk who had become a thief died soon afterwards, and they were all very sad. And within a short space of time, the two other men who had joined the boat later on also died after an accident.

Silently, the men walked down the path to the harbour, and at the place where the boat was moored there was a big basket with loaves and a barrel of water for the journey. Gratefully they carried it on board, unfastened the rope and sailed back out to sea.

A strong wind blew into the sails, and after a journey of several weeks they approached an island which was covered with such lush grass that it was bright green. There was no bare rock or barren patch to be seen. The monks landed and moored their boat by dropping the anchor. Again they had nothing to eat or drink. They quenched their thirst by a small stream, but could not see anything to eat.

"Friends," said Brendan, "today is Maundy Thursday, and in three days' time it will be Easter. If I'm right, there are some sheep grazing on the hills over there. God will permit us to prepare one of these for the Easter meal."

The monks went up into the hills and saw beautiful sheep as large as cows, with spotless white coats. They took one of the creatures, which was happy to go with them.

When they returned to Brendan they found a young man with him. He welcomed the monks to the island and had brought them a lot of bread and water. They thanked him, ate and drank, and loaded up the boat, when the young man said, "That's enough. In a week's time I will come back to you and bring some more food with me because you will stay here today and tomorrow, on Good Friday. On the morning of Easter Saturday, you will sail on to that small island that you can see over there in the sea. You will reach it in the evening. You can celebrate Easter there in the morning, and then sail on to an island where I will bring you food until after Pentecost."

Brendan was surprised that the young man knew when they would sail on and where they would go, but the latter laughed and said they would soon see that everything would happen as he had told them.

On Holy Saturday they sailed on to the small island, which they reached in the evening. The island was almost circular, and so small that there was only just room for the fifteen men to land. They slept there and on Easter morning they built their altar. Brendan took bread and wine and celebrated the holy feast of Easter with his friends. When they had celebrated, they all felt very happy. They sang together and looked out over the wide sea until they suddenly felt a shock wave running through the island. The water slowly rose up the shore, and one of the monks called out, "The island is sinking. Come quick, get in the boat!" The men jumped up, ran to the boat and climbed in. As the last monk climbed over the side, the water was lapping over the place where they had just celebrated Easter. Once they were safely in the boat and had recovered from the fright, they said, "Father Brendan, what is this? How is this possible?"

"Dear friends," said Brendan, "the island was the back of Jasconius, the biggest fish in the world. He swam here and was lying with his back above the water so that we could celebrate Easter. Look over there to the right in the water, and you will see him swimming."

The monks saw the mighty body and enormous tail as the fish quickly swam away from them.

"Now we will go on to the next place," said Brendan. "I can see some white birds flying over there. Let's follow them. They will surely lead us to the place where we can celebrate the next feast, the feast of Pentecost."

This is what happened. Like the first island, this island was also surrounded by rocks, but there was one place where a river flowed into the sea. They sailed in at that point, but the water dropped so steeply into the sea that they landed and pulled their boat with ropes, against the current. The white birds were still with them. They spoke with human voices and told them all about the things they would still encounter on their journey.

They stayed there until after Pentecost. The young man brought them enough food, so that they were able to go on with the boat well stocked up, and when their boat was finally at the mouth of the river once again, one of the birds sat in a branch of a tree above them and said, "You were with us in the paradise of birds. From now on you will sail for another seven years. Every year you will spend the holy feasts in the same place, from Maundy Thursday to Easter Saturday, on the island of the sheep, Easter on the back of Jasconius, Pentecost on our island, and the twelve holy days from Christmas to Epiphany, on the island of Albeus. That is where you are going now. I wish you a good journey. After seven years you will finally reach your goal. May God be with you. Farewell until we see you in a year's time."

Then the bird stretched its wings and flew back along the river over the island.

There was a long journey ahead, because they would not reach the island of Albeus until Christmas. They sailed through wild seas where danger lurked. However, before the little boat capsized in the sea, a bright light suddenly appeared one morning. The monks were still asleep, and only Brendan was awake. Before him stood the angel who had also told him before the journey that he would be with them always.

"Brendan," said the angel, "Remember what I said to you then. Don't forget it, not even when you are in the greatest danger."

When the angel had said this, he bade farewell to Brendan, blessed him and left.

Shortly afterwards, the autumn storms started and blew the little boat along. There were tremendous waves and the little boat, which was lightly built of pieces of wood covered with oxhide, was tossed about on the waves. Then they came to a place where the water started to swirl around. The monks could no longer keep hold of the rudder and the boat was drawn into a terrible whirlpool. It slipped further and further down into the whirling depths, until the monks feared that it would be sucked down to the bottom of the wild sea.

Then Brendan stood up and called out loudly in the howling wind, "You, wild storm, you, insatiable sea. If you want to pull us down, take me alone and leave the other men!"

Brendan got ready to jump into the water, but as soon as he had spoken, the wind dropped, the black clouds passed over and the whirlpool let go of the boat so that it drifted on in calmer waters. And so they were saved from drowning.

Another time they were sailing across a smooth sea in bright weather, when suddenly a gust of wind tugged at the sail and the boat keeled over dangerously. When they raised the mast again, Brendan looked up and saw a small dark man sitting in the mast, looking round with fiery red eyes.

"Where have you come from?" said Brendan.

"I come from the depths under the sea," answered the Devil.

"Is your kingdom there?" asked Brendan.

"Yes," said the Devil, "but now that you can see me, you can have a look at hell."

Then the devil waved his small crooked hand, and for a moment Brendan saw all the fire and violence, all the pain and suffering of the subterranean kingdom, down in the depths. Brendan could barely stop himself from covering his eyes.

"So, you holy men of God," screamed the Devil, "You are stronger than I thought. And your angel is close by, so I'd better go. But I'll be back." Once again a fierce gust of wind dipped the mast down to the waves, but when the boat righted itself, the black figure had disappeared.

For weeks afterwards the sea was very calm. At last, the monks sighed with relief when, on the darkest day of the year, they saw the island where they hoped to land after their long trip, lying before them in the distance.

Once again, they could sail up a river, which took them to the middle of the island. There they found a large chapel surrounded by small round huts which looked like beehives. They were the same sort of huts as those in which Brendan and his monks had lived in Ireland.

The abbot of the monastery, an old man with a long silvery-white beard and silvery white hair down to his shoulders, had seen them approaching and had walked to the mooring place to help them disembark. They had many questions, but he didn't answer any of them. He merely gestured with his hands and his face, and said nothing. He led them around the island and showed them all the buildings.

When the others had gone to sleep that night, the abbot took Brendan into his hut and started to speak.

He told him they had lived there for many, many years. When they had arrived, the hermit Albeus was still alive, and after his death they had stayed — he as abbot, with fourteen other monks. They had promised each other not to speak in the daytime, and to talk only at night.

"But why do you do that?" asked Brendan.

"Because we want to learn to listen to the language of the king of the elements. He speaks in the stars which move on their wide course, and in the wind and in the clouds. We also hear his voice in the powerful surf of the sea, and in the murmuring of the stream that flows through the woods. He speaks in the song of the birds and in all the animal noises. When it is quite silent outside, which often happens during the day, we hear the voice in our hearts, because God speaks outside us and within us. It is His language that we wish to learn to understand."

Brendan and his monks also stopped speaking during the days that they were on the island of Albeus from Christmas Eve, also known as Silent Night, until Epiphany. Then they prepared to travel on.

During the trip which they made, there was a time when the wind dropped at sea and it was so calm that there were not even any waves on the water. They sailed across an enormous, mirror-smooth stretch of water. When they were at sea for long periods, Brendan would perform the services and preach in the bows of the boat while the others sat by the rudder. One day, during the service, one of his comrades looked overboard into the water. At that moment the water became more transparent than ever before. Looking down into the depths, the monk suddenly saw large numbers of terrible monsters. There were dragons, squids and terrible creatures he didn't even know, all crawling around. They stretched out their claws and tentacles up to the boat.

The poor monk screamed out in fear and shouted to Brendan that he must lower his voice so that the boat would pass over this danger unnoticed, but Brendan carried on preaching without a pause, even more powerfully than before, and then the creatures moved away and sank back into the depths where they belonged.

So Brendan and his colleagues had many adventures and survived many dangers. After seven years, the moment they had been waiting for finally arrived.

The boat was sailing into a wall of fog and they knew they had to pass through the fog to reach the island of the saints. However, when they sailed into it, the fog was so thick that it was dark. They were amazed and joyful when Brendan's angel appeared in front of them, making a clear open path so that their boat pushed the fog to the right and to the left and they could follow the angel.

They sailed like this for three days, and on the fourth day they left the fog behind and saw the island of the saints ahead in all its splendour. The boat sailed into the small harbour and was moored. When the men disembarked, an old man in a shining white robe came up to them, guided them over the island and showed them many of its beauties: the gems which glittered at their feet, the fragrance of the blossom on the trees, and the light which was always radiant there.

When the old man had guided them all around the island, Brendan asked, "Tell us, honourable companion, what do we do now?"

"Brother Brendan," said the old man, "I must go on to where my work is in this paradise, but you may stay until the ninth hour of this day. When the bells ring, go back to your boat. Your angel will show you the way."

This is what happened. The angel was in the harbour and pointed the way to them.

"I must stay here" said the angel, "because this is the kingdom where I live."

Then the monks sailed through the fog without encountering further danger or difficulties, and after another three months they reached Ireland again.

# Nicholas of Myra

## What storms there are at sea

Nicholas was a rich man, respected in the city of Myra and through-out the land. Next to him lived a nobleman who had become poorer and poorer as the years passed.

This nobleman had three daughters, and there had been some important suitors who would have liked to marry them. The daughters also wished to marry a nobleman, but a girl must have a dowry to bring to her marriage, and they were so poor that they did not even have enough to eat.

One day, the father said, "Dear daughters, everything is gone. You will have to go into the countryside and ask the farmers whether you can herd their pigs."

The girls burst into tears when they heard that they would have to earn their keep by tending pigs, but they got ready to leave their father's home the next day.

Nicholas heard about the nobleman's troubles and decided to help him. He went to his cellar, found a nugget of gold, tied it up in a cloth, and when it was dark, he walked over to his neighbour's house. Softly he opened the window, threw in the gold and quickly walked back to his house, unseen by anyone.

The next morning the poor man found the gold. He called his daughters and they were all tremendously happy. They could buy food to eat, and above all they had a dowry, so the oldest daughter could marry. But it was not long before everything was gone again, and Nicholas, who realized this, found another piece of gold in his cellar and wrapped it up. Again, he waited for night to fall, secretly walked to his neighbour's house and threw the gold in through the window.

The next morning there was again great joy in the nobleman's family. There was food to eat, and the second daughter could get married. As before, the nobleman thanked God and the person who had given the gold. However, when they found themselves in great need yet again, and his third daughter wished to marry, the nobleman decided to spend the night in the downstairs room by the window. He hoped to find out who was giving him these riches.

That night, Nicholas took twice as much gold, and when he arrived at his neighbour's house he carefully dropped it inside. Nevertheless, there was a loud thump and the nobleman woke up with a start. He jumped up, lit the lamp and when he saw the open window and the package on the floor, he took the lamp and walked outside as quickly as he could. He was just able to catch up with the unknown giver of the gold before the latter reached his house.

In the light of his lamp, the nobleman recognized his neighbour, Nicholas. He bowed down deep, kissed his hand and thanked him from the depths of his heart. But Nicholas said, "Go and celebrate the marriage of your youngest daughter. Make sure it is a great feast, but do not tell anyone that it was I who brought you the gold."

This is how St Nicholas helped with the marriages of the three daughters. The people called him "the good marriage man."

## The strange sailor

What dreadful storms there are at sea. The wind whips up the waves higher and higher until they crash down on any ship which is unable to reach a harbour in time. The wind is so strong that it rips the sails to shreds and plucks men off the deck if they do not hold on very tight.

Once there was a ship in such a storm, but the sailors had experienced danger so often that they were no longer afraid. However, this time their ship was tossed to and fro so violently that they thought they would all perish. Then they thought of Nicholas and the stories told about him of helping people in distress at sea, so they called out, "Nicholas, strong helper, help us or we will perish!"

The wind carried their call, and when they looked up they saw a man on their ship who was working with great strength and skill. He knotted the sheets which had come loose and tied down new sheets to strengthen the mast. He also took down the sails that had been ripped, and hoisted up new sails. Then they heard his mighty call to the wind and the sea, and the ship slowly regained its course, the wind dropped and the sea became calmer. Finally, they noticed that the weather was clearing and that they were closer to the harbour. This gave them courage and confidence and they took hold of the rudder and sailed straight towards the haven. They were so busy that they didn't notice where the strange sailor had gone. They had no time to think about it because everyone was working hard until the ship was safely at anchor in the harbour. Then they looked at each other and said, "He was a true sailor. He did everything much better than we do. But the wind and the sea also listened to him. Could it have been St Nicholas?"

Then they disembarked and went together to the Church of St Nicholas nearby. The saint himself stood in front of the large church door and greeted the men. They didn't see his sailor's suit, but they recognized his face. It was above all his eyes, which laughed as though they wanted to say, "Yes, it was really me. I was with you in the storm."

The sailors did not doubt this. They bent down in front of him and thanked him, but Nicholas said, "If you had not called me, I could not have helped you. If you had not trusted in me, I couldn't have done anything. You were saved by your own faith."

## A hundred measures of grain

Sometimes a harvest can be good, and sometimes it is poor. Once the harvest was so poor in the country where Nicholas lived that the people were starving. Food was urgently needed, or many would die of hunger.

In those days, ships came into the harbour transporting grain, carrying their valuable cargo from Egypt to Rome. Nicholas heard this, went to the harbour, and said, "Please give us just a hundred measures of grain from every ship. If you do, the people can be saved from starvation."

The captains were afraid to agree to this, and they said, "Lord, in the city of Alexandria in Egypt, where we loaded the grain, it was measured and we must take the Emperor in Rome the exact quantity measured there, so we cannot give you anything. The Emperor would punish us."

However, Nicholas spoke to them sternly: "Do what I say, and God himself will make sure that the Emperor receives what was measured out for him in Alexandria. He will not get any less than what is owed him."

The sailors trusted Nicholas's word. They filled bags with a hundred measures of grain from every ship, and gave it to Nicholas. Then they sailed to Rome.

In Rome, the people who measured the Emperor's grain were waiting on the quayside. They went on to the ships and measured the grain when the ships were unloaded.

When everything had been unloaded, they called the captains and said, "You have done well. We have received the same amount of grain as that which was loaded up in Alexandria."

Then the sailors said, "Nicholas performed a miracle because none of the grain that we gave him is missing. God himself gave us back what we gave to the starving people."

As the ships were leaving the harbour in Nicholas's country to sail to Rome, he had divided the grain amongst the people in such a way that everyone got what they needed. It was not very much, but all the people had enough for two years, and there was even enough left so that they could sow the seed in the fields of that country.

## The magic oil

There was once an ugly witch who lived under the roots of an old tree. She was a real pest to the farmers in the neighbourhood. They almost always had to give her the best of the harvest, because otherwise she would destroy their land. When Nicholas heard this, he felt pity for the farmers, cut down the tree and pulled the roots from the ground so that the witch had to flee.

You can imagine how angry she was. There was no room for her in the farmers' fields, and so she crawled into a cave in the mountains. There she thought and thought, and finally came up with a way in which she could get revenge on Nicholas. She made a fire and brewed a magic oil that smelled very sweet, but was actually very dangerous. If you poured this oil out anywhere, it would burn with hot fierce flames.

One day, sailors who were sailing along the coast of Nicholas's country saw a boat coming towards them. There was an old woman in the boat, who asked them in an ingratiating voice if they would do something for her. Sailors are helpful people, and of course they were pleased to help her. The woman had such a beautiful soft voice. They helped her on board and she told them that she had wanted to go to Nicholas's church to honour him there, but that she had some urgent things to do and therefore, she was looking for friendly, helpful people who would go there in her place. All they had to do was to brush some of the oil she had in a bottle on the walls of the church to fill the church with a wonderful fragrance. That is how she wished to honour Nicholas. Moreover, she was a poor old woman and it was a long trip for her. The sailors took the bottle and said that they would do what she asked. Then they helped her back into her own boat and sailed on.

A little later, the ship's cabin boy said, "Oh! Where has she gone?"

The sailors looked all around in surprise, but there was nothing to be seen of the boat or the woman.

"She disappeared very quickly," the captain said thoughtfully. "Look," he called to the others, "here's another ship sailing towards us. Who is it this time?"

The boat came alongside and a man climbed on board who looked so much like Nicholas that no one dared to say a word and waited respectfully to see what he wanted.

He asked, "Was there a poor old woman here?"

"There certainly was," said the captain. "She was here a minute ago and then she suddenly disappeared."

"And did she give you anything?" asked Nicholas.

The sailors told the whole story about the bottle of oil, and Nicholas frowned and said, "That woman was a dangerous witch. I'll show you. Just give me that bottle."

The captain took the bottle out of his pocket and Nicholas opened it and poured the oil over the sea. As soon as it touched the water it flamed up like a torch. The flames were so fierce that the sailors quickly steered their boat away.

"And that's what was to be smeared on the walls of my church," said Nicholas. "Now you know who you spoke to and why she disappeared so quickly when I came."

The sailors realized that Nicholas had not only saved his church, but also saved them, because they would have been caught in the flames if they had used the oil. They thanked him and said, "Nicholas, always be with us when we are in danger and distress."

## The Roman princes

In the days of the Roman Empire, the people revolted against the Emperor of Rome. The Emperor then sent out three princes with their armies to fight the rebels and subdue them. These leaders were called Nepotianus, Ursus, and Apulio. They set sail from Rome and wished to sail to the country of the rebellious people across the sea, but they were caught in a storm and the ships were blown off course, and they were forced to land in a harbour, close to the town of Myra, where Nicholas lived.

Nicholas invited the princes to have a meal with him. He wanted to ask them to prevent their soldiers from pillaging the land and stealing the people's food, as Roman soldiers so often did.

As they sat at the table and talked about this, it happened that not far away, the governor had condemned to death three innocent knights. When Nicholas heard about this, he immediately left the table and asked his three guests to go with him.

At great speed, they rode to the place where the knights were to be executed. When they arrived, the knights were already kneeling down, with their heads bowed, and the executioner had raised his sword to chop off their heads. Nicholas jumped down from his horse, ran to the executioner and seized his sword and threw it a long way away. Then he freed the prisoners from their chains, and went with them and the princes to the governor's palace. When he arrived, he pushed back the doors forcefully and walked into the palace, where the governor hastily came up to him.

Nicholas spoke to him angrily, with strong words: "You wanted to execute three honest and just knights, even though they had not been brought to justice. And I know why. Their enemy promised you a large sum of money if you had them beheaded. You wanted to make yourself rich and you were very unjust to these men. You allowed yourself to be bribed. You are an unworthy governor. Should I submit a complaint about your unworthy behaviour to your Emperor in Rome?"

Nicholas continued in this vein for a while, until the three princes asked forgiveness on behalf of the poor man. Then Nicholas fell silent and looked at the knights. When they were able to forgive the governor as well, he shook the governor's hand and they made peace.

The princes had to sail on with their ships. They were blessed by Nicholas, sailed on and were able to subdue the rebels in a short time without spilling any blood. When they returned to Rome, they were welcomed back by the Emperor with great honour and wonderful gifts.

However, there are jealous and treacherous men everywhere, even in Rome. There were men who did not think the princes deserved to be so richly rewarded by the Emperor, and they promised the Emperor's advisor a lot of money if he could sow suspicion in his heart about these princes. The advisor, who wanted the money, went to the Emperor, and said that the three princes had become arrogant and that they no longer wanted to serve him, but wanted the throne for themselves. They were planning to come and murder the Emperor any day.

This was all lies, but the Emperor didn't know that. He was so furious with the princes that he had them seized and thrown into the dungeons. They were to be beheaded the next day without a trial. The poor princes were chained up with heavy chains. They had heard that they were to be executed and didn't know how to let the Emperor know that they were innocent. They sat side by side, in great sorrow.

Suddenly one of them, Nepotianus, sat up. "Do you remember how Nicholas punished the governor when we were on our trip because he wanted to execute those three innocent knights? Let us pray to Nicholas. Perhaps he will help us."

That night, the Emperor Constantine slept badly, because he was plagued by a terrible dream. There was a man in front of him who called out, "Why did you imprison those three princes, the princes who risked their lives for you on their distant journey? Why did you condemn them without hearing them? Get up quickly and release them, or I will ask God to battle with you, and then you will die and your body will be thrown to wild animals."

Then the Emperor asked, "Who are you to come into my palace at night and speak to me so angrily?"

The saint answered, "I am Nicholas, a bishop from the city of Myra."

He appeared in the same way to the advisor who had made the false accusations about the princes, and he said, "You unworthy man. You are not worthy to live. Why do you abuse the Emperor's trust to have three innocent men executed? Go to the Emperor immediately and advise him to release them or you will die and your house will be destroyed."

The advisor asked, "Who are you to threaten me so terribly?"

The saint answered, "Know that I am Nicholas, a bishop from the city of Myra."

Early next morning, the Emperor and his advisor met and told each other about their dreams. Then the Emperor quickly had the prisoners brought to him, and asked them, "What sort of magic is this which means that the advisor and I were both threatened in our dreams?"

"We do not know anything about magic," they answered, "and we would like to say we are innocent."

"Do you know a man called Nicholas?" asked the Emperor.

When the princes heard this name they exclaimed, "Oh, if Nicholas were here he would be able to save us. Nicholas, please save us in our time of need!"

The Emperor released them and asked them to go to Nicholas and offer him gifts in the name of the Emperor, so that the saint would not threaten the Emperor in future, but would help him in his heavy task of ruling the great Roman Empire. "And thank God," he said, "that he saved you from death through his servant Nicholas."

The princes did what they were ordered and told everyone around the story of how Nicholas had helped them.

## The king's servant

After Nicholas died, the people continued to call on him when they were in distress, and he helped them. There was a man and a woman who had no children, and after they waited for a long time and still hadn't had a child, they called on St Nicholas.

Shortly afterwards the woman became pregnant, and less than a year later a son was born to her and they called him Adeodatus. After that, these parents celebrated the birth of St Nicholas every year on the fifth of December, to thank him for the son they had had with his help.

There was a war with a neighbouring country and the soldiers of the enemy invaded the country and even their house. They took Adeodatus with them to become their king's servant. When it was St Nicholas's Day the following year, Adeodatus' father and mother again celebrated it. Adeodatus himself was serving a banquet to his king that day, and when he passed him a precious beaker, he thought of his father and mother and remembered that it was the day of St Nicholas and that there would be a great feast celebrated in his home. He felt so sad that he was now living here as a servant in captivity, that he put down the beaker and sighed deeply. The king looked at him and said severely, "Why are you sighing? Are you sad? Tell me, what's the matter?"

Adeodatus did not want to answer, but the king insisted: "I want you to tell me why you sighed so deeply. Tell me, or I will have you beaten until you speak."

Then Adeodatus told him what he was thinking about and why he was so sad. The king said harshly, "Your Nicholas has nothing to do with me. You are my servant and you stay here."

At that moment a terrible whirlwind rose up. It blew powerfully through the castle and lifted Adeodatus from his place. It carried him up through the air and then dropped him in front of his parents' house, still holding the beaker. Then he went inside and celebrated with them the feast which he had wanted to attend so much.

Da waren münche inne,
die dienten got mit sinne,
die alten und die jungen
Lassen und sungen.

# Gall

## Bear, fetch wood for the fire!

Gall was a strong, broad-shouldered man. His face was framed by a red beard and red hair. Some people were afraid of him, while others loved him. When he said yes, he meant yes, and when he said no, he meant no.

In the south of Germany, by Lake Constance, he said yes to that country, and to those people, and no to his own friend and teacher. And that was hard.

Gall lay in his hut with a raging fever, on a bed of grass and ferns. His body glowed, his heart beat loudly, but his thoughts were clear and strong.

In front of him stood the abbot, Columbanus, a strict, upright and stately figure. His hair was greying, but he was not yet bowed down with age. He had just heard from Gall that the latter did not want to travel any further with him to the country over the Alps.

Columbanus was angry because he could not do without his companion on that long trip.

"Up to now you have followed me everywhere," said Columbanus. "From distant Hibernia, through Britain over the sea to Gaul, and then here to this lake. You are ten years younger than I. You are stronger and you speak the language of the people better. I need you! Why will you not go on with me? You owe me obedience. What is your reason? Are you afraid of the high mountains, the ice and the snow?"

Gall said, "You know, Columbanus, that I am not afraid of cold or heat, or hard work. It is the country and the people that keep me here. Moreover, I have been ill for a long time. I could not walk ten steps."

"I order you to come with me," Columbanus said vehemently.

"My body is weak and orders me to stay here," said Gall, "and I feel that that is right."

When Columbanus saw that his friend was determined, he took a step backwards and said, "You will not obey me and so I must punish

173

you for this. You will no longer perform the holy sacrament at the altar as long as I live."

They were both silent for a long time, until Gall said, "I accept your punishment, although it is a very heavy one. Now that you are going I thank you for everything you have done for me. My thoughts will always be with you. Farewell."

"Farewell," said Columbanus, and he left the hut and started on his way.

And so Gall remained behind on his own. Friendly people in the area helped him, and he was cured and regained his strength. At last, he decided to find the place where he would live in that country. He took the small fishing boat which he had sailed on the lake many times, looking for a suitable place to live.

"Lord," he asked quietly in his heart, "show me the place where I can live."

As he sat waiting in the boat, rocking on the water and thinking of this, a fish eagle rose up from the shore and flew to the mountains on the other side, beating its wings. Then the wind carried him up and he circled above the forests, in the place where the sun rises in summer.

Gall felt joy in his heart. He sailed the boat to the shore, gave it to the fisherman to whom it belonged and started his trip. The path by the lake came to a rocky path which led upwards.

On this trip he was joined by a companion he had met, called Hiltibud. Together, they went on their way.

Hiltibud knew the area and Gall asked him whether the place where he had seen the eagle would be a good place for them to live. It had to be a lonely place, because Gall wished to live in silence.

"Lord, it is certainly lonely," answered Hiltibud, "but there are also many bears and snakes and wolves."

"Don't worry," said Gall, "they will disappear, or help us."

The two men walked on without interruption, and by nine o'clock, they still had not had anything to eat. Hiltibud asked if they could rest for a while and have something to eat, but Gall answered, "No, I will go on now until I have found the place where we can stay."

This took a while, but at last they came to the River Steinach. At this place the river cascaded down from a great height and had eroded a deep pool in the rocks. The water flowed into a large basin and then flowed out again down the mountain.

In that place there was also a lot of green grass. It was a small meadow, surrounded by trees. Hiltibud sat down exhausted and saw

Gall walking into the meadow, but at the edge of the wood, his foot became entangled in thorns and he fell over. Gall was unable to stand up by himself, and so Hiltibud went to him. "Give me your hand, Lord, and I will help you to stand up."

"No, Hiltibud. Never mind," said Gall, "we won't go on. We will find peace here for ever. I want to live here because this is the place I have chosen."

Dusk was already falling, and they built a simple hut with branches. They made a fire and they had something to eat and drink in the light of the setting sun. Then they put the remainder of the food by the fire and lay down in the hut to rest.

Night fell, but the moon shone so brightly above the meadow that Hiltibud could see a large brown bear walking to the fire from the edge of the wood. He grabbed the remaining food with his paws and started to eat it. To Hiltibud's surprise, Gall stood up, walked to the bear, stood in front of it and said, "Bear, you are a wild animal and you are stealing what is not yours. In the name of Christ, Our Redeemer, I order you to go to the wood and fetch wood for this fire. If you do that, I will give you food to eat."

Hiltibud sat down, and to his surprise, he saw that the mighty creature turned round and trotted away. After a little while, the bear came back with a huge piece of wood, and placed it on the fire.

"You have done exactly as I asked you," said Gall, and he took a piece of bread and gave it to the bear to eat. "Now go, and don't disturb us again tonight. Come back tomorrow and we will share our bread with you, if you bring us what we ask."

This is what happened. When the two men started to build their permanent hut, the creature came out of the woods again and brought them the timber they needed. The bear ate the bread it was given and never stole anything from the monks again.

They worked hard on the hut, and the men in the valley who had heard the sound of their axe and their hammer, came to help them. They put four posts in the corners in the ground. Then they secured the planks which had been cut from the trunks with the axe. All the planks fitted exactly, apart from one which was too short.

"How can that be?" asked Hiltibud.

"The trunk was too short and there was an enormous knot at the end which broke off," said one of the men. "What is missing is four times the breadth of my hand."

But Gall came up and told the men to come because he had

prepared food and it was ready. So they ate fish, carrots and fruit and Gall gave thanks for all the gifts from the wood.

They soon noticed that they had received even more than they knew, because when they tried again to fit the plank that had been too short before the meal, one of the men cried, "Look, it's sticking out at this end. It's six inches too long."

"Don't cut it to size," said Gall, "leave it sticking out. This wood is very special."

That is what the men did, and from then on they followed Gall's instructions very closely, because they realized that God's word worked through him.

Gall lived in that place for many years, and the wild animals were no longer wild and did not hurt anybody. The bear helped with its great strength, and ate bread from Gall's hand. Only the snakes who had lived there before Gall had arrived, had fled and were never seen again.

Once there were many unexpected guests to talk to Gall and ask his advice. They had come from far away and had not had anything to eat for a long time. Hiltibud went to the river to catch fish. Despondently he lowered his net into the water; he had never caught many fish and they had always been small.

But this time, as soon as he had put out his net, he noticed a strong movement in the water above at the top of the stream. Two otters were chasing a large fish through the water, and it swam quickly down the river to escape the sharp teeth of its enemies. It swam straight into Hiltibud's net.

There was an enormous pull. Hiltibud almost fell over, but was just able to grab the net with both hands. He got to his feet and needed all his strength to pull the jumping fish on to land. Wet through, and covered in cuts, but very happy with the large fish, he went back to the hut. Of course they had a wonderful meal and there was more than they could eat.

When Gall was very old, a servant from the castle of Arbon, came to him and asked him if he would go to the castle.

"Right down to the castle by the lake?" asked Gall. "I can't manage that any more. My legs are old and stiff. But why do you want me to go down there?"

"There is a sick man and no one can cure him. We know that your word has the strength to heal people," said the servant.

Gall sighed, stood up and went down with the servant. At the bend in the road, he turned to Hiltibud and said, "My good friend, I am ninety-five years old. If I die, have my body placed on a cart drawn by wild horses. They will bring me here because the wild animals know where I live."

Slowly they walked down, step by step, day by day, until they reached the castle of Arbon. Everyone was glad that Gall had made the trip. At the same time they were worried because he was old and very tired.

Every day, Gall sat by the sick man until his fever abated and he slowly regained his health. But at the same time, Gall had to lie down and could no longer get up. He became quieter and paler, and said less and less, until one morning the people in the castle were woken up, because large flocks of songbirds were singing in the trees around the house, singing and trilling with all their might, so loudly that the people could not hear each other speak.

When the lord of the castle and his wife went outside to see what this meant, all the birds spread their wings and flew up into the sky, higher and higher, until you could not see them any more.

In Gall's room the sunlight fell through the windows on to his face. Nothing moved, but he seemed to listen to the disappearing song of the birds, and that morning, he died.

Hiltibud remembered what his master had told him, and said that a cart must be brought. The bier with Gall's body should be placed on the cart and two wild horses must draw the cart. They would take him where he wanted to go.

The lord of the castle trusted Hiltibud's word. When the cart was ready, and his servants had saddled two fiery horses, stamping their hooves, the bier was placed on the cart. The horses were released and they pulled the cart quickly straight into the mountains and up to the River Steinach, where they stopped. The men who had followed the wild horses as quickly as possible, removed the bier from the cart and unharnessed the horses.

Gall's body was placed in the small hut. There was a candle by his head, and a candle by his feet. Both candles burned with a bright flame and did not get any smaller, even after several days. Everyone who went there and saw the light felt great joy in their hearts, and blind people who came even had the light restored to their eyes.

The horses remained in the meadow quietly, as though they felt that their lord was no longer with them. It was only when Gall's body was buried in a place covered with grass and flowers that they left for the fields and hills where other wild creatures lived.

# Dionysius

## They felt the earth tremble

The city of Heliopolis, in Syria, was in uproar. There were groups of people huddled together everywhere, in the squares and on the corners of the streets. Sometimes they whispered, their heads close together, looking suspiciously left and right. Others could be heard making powerful speeches, ostentatiously showing off their colourful, wide cloaks and gesturing excitedly. Here and there, some people raised their fists secretly and there were even some brawls. When the sharp clip-clopping of hooves was heard on the cobbles and a group of soldiers approached on horseback, the troublemakers dispersed in every direction, to meet again further on.

In front of the west gate of the city there were two guards standing stoutly to the left and right of the gate, wearing their helmets and harnesses, their lances planted in the ground, and their shields on their left arm.

"By my beard, Yefrem," growled the guard on the right, "if that isn't our courier approaching in the distance, then my name isn't Jared."

The two men gazed intently at the horseman who was galloping up at great speed.

"You're right," said Yefrem, "he's covered the distance to Athens and back faster than I thought. Could he have found one of the Greek judges to help us with our troubles here? The city has been in uproar for days now."

"Do you know what happened exactly?" asked Jared.

"Yes, I do," said Yefrem, "I was standing right by it. It started during the celebrations last week. So many people gathered together in the square in front of the temple that it became more and more crowded. I was pushed to the side with the group where I was standing, right into the pillar with the marble statue of the god Serapis. The priest they are so angry with now, was pressed against the pillar by the crowd and it fell over. The statue of the god broke into pieces on the ground.

"Well you know what it's like. Everybody blames everybody else. If the guard in the square hadn't intervened, they would have executed the priest then and there. They took him with them and locked him up in a dungeon. At least he was safe there. But the people are excited because they have asked for a judge to come from Athens. I'm very curious. Move over, the horseman is coming and must get through quickly."

The courier who had reached the gate, reined in his horse and greeted the guards.

"Oh, yes," said Jared agreeably. "We know you. You can enter the city if you can just tell us if help is coming."

"It certainly is," said the horseman, who had to get his breath back and rubbed the dust from his eyes. "The new young judge, Dionysius, has been sent here. He left immediately, and if I'm not mistaken he will be arriving today, so let me through! The governors' palace has to know the news quickly so that they can prepare everything for his arrival."

"He's in a hurry," said Yefrem when the horseman had ridden on. "Look how his horse is raising sparks from the cobbles."

There was good reason for his haste because the young judge was following with his retinue almost as quickly as the courier, and he arrived at the city in the evening.

The people had swept the streets and decorated them with branches and flowers. Now they crowded on the broad city walls, curious to see the judge arrive.

When the procession came riding up over the hills in their shining cloaks, sparkling in the evening sun, everyone had something to say.

"He's a very important judge."

"He was educated in the holy site of Eleusis."

"That means he knows everything there is to know."

"He's certainly a good horseman, they can hardly keep up with him."

"What a beautiful man!"

Dionysius reined in his horse at the gate and his retinue also came to a halt. The men, women, children and old people looked on with great respect and saw the judge greeting everyone on the walls by raising his hand. The soldiers gestured to him to wait, and then the city governors came out of the gate to welcome the important guest.

That very evening, Dionysius heard and saw so much in the city that he wished to carry out the judgement the next morning, in the square in front of the temple of Serapis where the statue had broken in pieces.

In the morning, he sat down on the raised judge's chair after a short night's sleep. Next to him were the city governors, the councillors and the soldiers, while the people crowded in front of him. Over their heads, he could see the mighty rock walls against which the city had been built. The court case went just as Dionysius had imagined, and being a good judge, he listened to everyone.

By six o' clock it was absolutely silent in the square, because the moment had come for Dionysius to pronounce judgement. However, at that moment the people felt the earth tremble under their feet. At the same time, the sun in the sky was eclipsed, and it was so dark that no one could see their neighbour because even the light of the stars was extinguished.

Everyone held his breath in fear, and no one dared to say anything, and in this silence the people felt that the trembling of the earth became even more violent. They heard the mountains cracking with a roar and on all sides the roofs of the houses collapsed and the walls fell down,

A dreadful wailing and moaning rose up from the city, and continued for a long time until the ninth hour when the earth calmed down, the darkness withdrew and the sun shone again. There were people lying on the ground, pale and frightened, and they got up slowly and hesitantly. Dionysius himself sat down in his judge's seat again. He saw the people, the riven mountains, the collapsed houses and the many marble statues of gods that had fallen from their pillars. He was filled with a profound sense of wonder.

Hesitantly, the governor of the city asked what this meant, and because he didn't know, he asked them to bring him the Book of Numbers. He knew this book well from the days when he had lived with the priests in the holy place of Eleusis when he was a boy. This book contained everything about the course of the sun, the moon and the stars, but nothing he read could explain what had happened here in Heliopolis. He put the book aside and bowed his head. Then his heart told him, "You should not look in the sky, but direct your thoughts to the earth."

"Fetch me the Book of Spheres," he commanded quickly, and as he thought intently, the book was respectfully placed on his knees. For a while, his attention was completely taken up with the vision of a dark hill, a place of execution with three crosses on it. There were two robbers hanging on the crosses to the left and right, but on the middle cross there was someone who was more than a man. Dionysius heard the words, "This is the hidden God who has come to earth without the people noticing. He lived amongst us as a man, although He is the creator of all beings, visible and invisible. His unknowing executioners crucified him on the cross you see before you."

When Dionysius had seen this, he raised his head and again saw the people who looked at him silently, expecting an answer from him. He stood up and said, "God Himself has appeared on earth and has become a man. At this very hour, people have crucified Him and He has died. That is why the earth shook and the land was shrouded in darkness."

When Dionysius had said this, he fell silent. The governors, the wise men, the priests and the people were also silent. They heard the words which the judge spoke to them, but they couldn't understand them.

Dionysius did not understand either. However, later on when he returned home, his scribe wrote down everything which he had experienced in Heliopolis. After his death, this account was kept in the temple of Athena.

Dionysius remembered what he had seen and heard in his heart. He only asked what it meant when Paul of Tarsus visited Athens fourteen years later and told him for whom the earth had trembled and for whose death the sun had disappeared in darkness.

That was Paul's story and can be found in the book written by Luke, and that book can be found in the great Book which describes all the secrets of light and dark.

# Radegund

## On my word, Lord

Radegund was a German princess from the land of Thüringen. When she was just thirteen years old, she was abducted by King Chlotar of the Franks to his castle, where he forced her to stay until she reached adulthood and he married her.

Radegund knew that getting married meant being faithful, and she promised him, "I will always be faithful to you as long as you are faithful to me and the only brother I still have. Do not hurt him or me, and I will stay with you."

King Chlotar loved her very much and did not hurt her or her brother for many years. One day, he could no longer tolerate the fact that her brother's land was more beautiful than his and that her brother had more friends than he. In a burst of jealous rage, he sought a quarrel with Radegund's brother and killed him.

Radegund, who heard about this from a servant, fled from the castle. She no longer wanted to stay with Chlotar, who had slain her brother.

As she had left the castle very early in the morning, she had already gone a long way before Chlotar noticed that she had gone. When he realized, he immediately saddled his horse and pursued her as quickly as he could.

Meanwhile, she had come to a field where a farmer was busy sowing oats. Radegund spoke to the farmer and said, "Farmer, you must help me. If my husband the king rides up, you must tell him that no one has come by since you started sowing the oats."

The farmer did not know whether he could do this, but to his great surprise the oats he had just sown were already shooting up and growing more and more quickly, until the ears were standing in the field ripe and ready to harvest.

Just as Radegund had managed to hide in the field of oats, and the shining ears bent over her protectively, King Chlotar came galloping up at full speed, because he had followed his wife's trail. As soon as the king saw the farmer, he reined in his horse and called out to ask if anyone had passed by.

"Lord," answered the farmer, "as I live, no one has passed by since I sowed these oats. On my word, Lord."

For a moment Chlotar looked at the tall oats in surprise because they were ripe in the field in the spring. Then he turned round and rode back to the castle.

This is how Radegund was saved by the farmer and by the miracle of the fast growing oats.

# Joan of Arc

## I am just a peasant girl

It was a warm summer's day. Joan stood in the garden next to the farm where she lived, holding a large bunch of white, yellow and red flowers. She breathed quickly because she had been running very fast, but as she stood there, she looked around in surprise. Hadn't she heard a voice telling her that her mother was calling her?

She had gone straight to her mother who was working in the kitchen, but she was busy and hadn't called Joan. Then she went into the garden where her father was working, but he also shook his head when she asked him whether he had called. Who had called her, then?

When she turned round, facing the high wall of the village church where she wanted to take the flowers, she again heard the voice calling her name. She looked up and saw a powerful figure. In her heart she knew that it was an angel, and she cast down her eyes because of the glow of light which radiated from him.

"Joan," she heard him say, "your country, France, is in dire need. It is occupied by the soldiers of the King of England. Your motherland must be freed. You must go to the crown prince of France and fight for him against the English."

Joan heard these words and tried to understand them. She thought about them for a while, and when she looked up, the angel had disappeared.

She didn't talk to anyone about it, but one evening she asked at home, "Father, what is a crown prince?"

"It's the oldest son of a king," her father said. "Later, he will be crowned king himself. It is the prince who will one day wear the crown of the king. That is why he is called the crown prince."

"Does our country have a crown prince?" she asked.

"Yes," answered her father, "and he lives in the great castle of Chinon, on the river Loire, but as long as the English soldiers are in France, he will probably never be crowned. Dear child, we poor peasants can't even read or write. What do we know of crown princes and kings? Go to sleep, because tomorrow you must get up early to milk the cows and clean the stable."

Autumn came, followed by winter and then spring. Once again the angel appeared to Joan and said, "I told you that your country of France is in dire need. Joan, you are the one who can free the land. Time presses. I am the archangel Michael, and I am ordering you to go to the crown prince."

"Michael," said Joan, "I am just a poor peasant girl and only thirteen years old. Why don't you ask a brave knight to do this work? Why are you asking me?"

"I am asking you, Joan, because you can hear me," said the angel, "I can tell you what you must do."

But then Joan's mother called her to the kitchen and the girl hurried to help her. There was a great deal of work that day and in the following days, and Joan always had to help. It was only in the evening before she went to sleep that she had time to think about what the angel had asked her. It was three years later, on Joan's sixteenth birthday, that the angel appeared to her again. He spoke to her sternly and insistently: "Joan, go to your uncle now. He will give you a horse. Ride to Charles, the crown prince, and remember that I will always be with you. I will answer any questions you want to ask. If you do as I say, you will free France and the prince will be crowned."

The following night, Joan decided to leave. She got up very early in the morning, dressed and went downstairs. At the door of her father and mother's bedroom, she whispered, "Farewell." Outside the animals' barn she waved them farewell, and by the gate of the courtyard, she said farewell softly to the dog. Then she went to her uncle.

She rode his horse to the royal court in Chinon, and gained an audience with the crown prince. She told him that the king of heaven, Michael himself, had sent her to help him free France from the enemy.

The crown prince looked at her and said, "But did you know that the enemy is much stronger than we are?"

Joan answered, "Michael said that he would help us."

Again the crown prince asked, "How can you, a peasant girl, lead an army and fight with knights?"

"Michael will fight for us," said Joan. "Trust in him."

A long time passed, but one day the crown prince said that Joan could lead the fight with all the French knights against the English enemy.

A tailor came to make a beautiful cloak for her, and the ladies of the court sewed a colourful banner with the Archangel Michael embroidered in gold thread. The stable master found his best horse for Joan and the armourer made her a wonderful harness.

"The sword is there already," she said mysteriously.

"How is that? Where is it?" everyone wanted to know.

"Michael himself has shown me where it is. It is in the village of Fierbois, close by, deep under the ground. Have the men dig behind the altar in the church and they will find the sword."

The men did dig under the stone floor, through the roots of trees and solid rocks until the sword was finally found in the depths of the earth. There was no rust on it, and it shone brightly in the light. Everyone was astonished and delighted at the same time and many people cried, "Michael himself preserved his sword for her in the earth."

When Joan raised the sword so that it sparkled in the sunlight, the soldiers chanted:

> See, there shines Michael's sword.
> And where his sword is,
> He himself is there too.
> Let us go.
> He gives us strength and courage,
> So that we will conquer.

Then the French knights marched against the enemy, and finally they successfully defeated the English and drove them from the country.

When the country had been freed, Joan rode with the crown prince to the city of Reims where the king's crown was kept. The prince was crowned and henceforth he was the king of France, a free country.

Joan stood next to the king. She carried the banner high above the heads of the people. Everyone could see the figure of Michael embroidered in gold thread. He had saved France through Joan and would henceforth protect the freedom of their country.

# Cuthbert

## They are like the snow

In the hills of Northumbria, in the north of England, there was a large house on the road running from the east to the west. There were rooms on every side, and everyone who lived there could look out over the land through his own window. Year after year, he could watch the spring, the summer and the autumn pass over the land — the spring with its bright flowers, the summer with its tall grasses in the green meadows and little fluffy clouds, and the autumn with its storms.

But now it was winter and it had just snowed. Everything was white, the hills, the bare trees, and the road leading up to the front door of the house.

A friendly old man was by the front door, making sure that it was properly shut. This was Cuthbert, a holy man, who had just come downstairs to the large dining hall in the middle of the house. They had told him that a guest had arrived, and therefore he had gone to have a look at the big oak door, but the front door was quite shut.

When Cuthbert turned round and walked into the dining hall, he could not see very much in the semi-darkness of the early winter morning, and so he did not notice that there was a boy seated on a bench in the corner opposite the entrance, until he was in the middle of the dining hall. The boy was wearing a thin cloak and was gazing quietly into space.

Cuthbert wondered where on earth he had come from. He was not one of the people who lived in the house. He must have walked all night through the snow from the distant village, and now he was having a rest.

Cuthbert fetched a bowl of water and his young guest washed his hands. Then he knelt down next to him, took off his shoes and socks and washed his feet, as was the custom. Then he took first one foot, and then the other, and dried them.

"You must be hungry," he said to the boy, "but I will have to ask you to wait until noon, when the meal is prepared."

The boy nodded, leant back and indicated that he was happy to wait.

Towards twelve o' clock, Cuthbert went back to the hall and while the others were laying the tables, he said to his guest, "Well, it will not be long. I'm just going to the kitchen. They will have taken the loaves out of the ovens. I will be back soon with a fresh loaf."

Cuthbert walked to the kitchen, picked up a large loaf and wrapped it in a cloth, because it was still hot. Then he walked back to the hall.

He stood still in surprise and looked at the corner opposite the door, but he couldn't see anyone. He turned around and looked along every wall, but the benches were empty. The boy must have gone outside. It had been too long for him to wait. Cuthbert put away the bread, walked to the heavy door and slowly opened it. In front of him there was a blanket of virgin snow quite untouched, without a single footprint.

As Cuthbert shut the door again, shaking his head, he suddenly smelled a fragrance of bread such as he had never experienced before. It was a delicate, beautifully sweet fragrance, and then he saw that by the door there were three loaves, so pure and white that no one on earth could have made them.

Then Cuthbert understood; this is how angels come to the people. They want to know whether the people are really willing to share their food and their homes, and then they give the people heavenly nourishment, because they are not able to eat the bread of earth.

They do not leave any footprints behind them. They are like the snow which falls from heaven and human eyes cannot follow their traces.

Cuthbert's hands trembled when he picked up the loaves and gave each of the men a piece of bread. No one had ever tasted sweeter or finer bread, because the angels only rarely come down to share their food with men.

# Luke the Evangelist

## My eyes saw

Luke the painter had worked on the painting of Mary for many days. For hours and hours he had painted her voluminous blue cloak with his broad brush until it completely enveloped her. The cloak was around her head, around her whole figure, right down to her feet. It fell around her in ample folds.

The cloak was open at her neck so that you could see the red robe underneath. As red as the roses in the hedge of my garden, thought Luke, when he finished off the edges by her neck with a finer brush. Above this was the face with the narrow, arched eyebrows, showing Mary's sense of wonder.

"And should I not be full of wonder?" the painter heard a voice say behind him. Mary herself had come in. She had often sat there so that Luke could paint her and in between times, he had worked on, on his own. Now that he was finishing off the brush-strokes, she came in again and looked over Luke's shoulder.

"Who wouldn't feel a sense of wonder, if they had seen as much as I have?" said Mary. Luke was silent. He put down the brush with the red paint, picked up the finest brush he had and made the blue in the eyes even deeper, and the light shining in them even brighter. Then he put down his last brush, and took a few steps back so that he could see the effects better.

"My eyes saw the Archangel Gabriel, who told me that I would be the mother of Jesus," Mary said softly. "They saw Jesus Himself for all the years that He lived, and once they saw the mighty Michael when heaven opened, and he pierced the savage dragon and threw him down on earth. My eyes have seen what is in heaven, what is on earth and what is under the earth. How well you have painted all this, Luke."

Mary walked up and took the painting into her hands for a moment. Then she turned round and left the room.

It was this painting which was later placed in the large church of Santa Maria Maggiore in the city of Rome. It remained there for centuries after Luke had painted it. It was as though Mary herself looked down from the painting at the thousands of people who had looked up at her throughout the ages.

When she looked at unhappy people they felt consoled. Those who were worn down with care, felt freed from their cares and the sick noticed that they were filled with new strength and felt much healthier. But the eyes which had seen so much not only had healing and consoling strength, they could also be piercingly strict.

Once a man came into the chapel whose heart was full of anger and spite. He carried a long sharp knife under his coat, and he came looking for trouble and prepared for violence.

He knelt amongst the others and pretended to pray, but in the meantime his hand groped for the handle of his knife. However, when he looked up for a moment, he was struck by a look in the eyes of the painting. The light in Mary's eyes burnt into his own eyes so fiercely that he was struck blind. In this way, the people were saved from the terrible deeds which this man would otherwise have committed, and he walked outside feeling the walls and full of malice.

When he returned to the same place much later, he left his knife at home, and standing under the painting he realized that his anger was slowly ebbing away and that Mary could also heal and console him.

# John the Evangelist

## The strength of the poison abated

Before Christ went up to heaven, He sent his disciples out into all the countries of the world. They were sent there to help the people and cure the sick in His name. John set off, and wherever he could help or cure people, he did so, and would spread the name of his master, because it was through His strength that the people's health could be restored.

The Romans said to John, "Our Emperor has forbidden the practice of healing people in Christ's name. You may not do this any more, and if you do, then you will be punished."

John knew that his Lord was more powerful than the Roman Empire and so he did not take any notice of their words and laid hands on even more of the sick than he had done before.

Roman soldiers seized John at the command of their leader, and brought him by ship to the great city of Rome. An enormous fire was being built in front of the Latin Gate. Above this, the soldiers hung a vat of oil. When the oil boiled, the soldiers immersed John in the vat.

The people who were standing around wept because they thought that John would burn, but when the fire was extinguished and the vat was lowered to the ground, John stood up and got out of the oil, and he spoke to the people as before. He was just as healthy as when he had been immersed in the vat.

The soldiers treated him with great awe and respect, because the heat had not had any power over John, and they let him go wherever he wanted.

Amongst the heathens there was a priest who told John, "I see that you can cure the people. However, I will only really trust what you do, if you dare to drink the poison in the cup which I am holding in my hand."

"The poison will not have any power over me." answered John.

"He who protected me from the heat of the boiling oil, will also remove the strength of this poison."

Then John picked up the cup with his left hand. With his right hand he made the sign of the cross over it. At that moment, the people standing round saw a snake slither out of the drink and over the edge of the cup to crawl away outside.

And thus the strength of the poison abated in the drink and John put the cup to his mouth and emptied it.

Some people thought he would fall down dead. Others, who had seen the snake slithering out of the cup, realized that the evil had disappeared from the drink. When John did not fall down, but simply gave the cup back to the priest, they cried, "You are strong, John, to be able to withstand the heat of the oil and the poison."

"No," said John, "the Lord who protects me against any heat and any poison is strong."

The people trusted in him and believed in the words which he spoke to them.

# Appendix

## Biographical information

**Agnes** (21 January)
There is very little historical information available about Agnes. She felt a vocation to follow Christ when she was only a small child. When she was twelve or thirteen years old, she rejected a young suitor who wished to marry her. In third century Rome, Christians could not yet openly practise their faith. The suitor she had rejected had her brought before the judge because of her devotion to Christ. Agnes defied her judges and torturers and gladly ascended the scaffold where she was to die by the sword. Her relics can be found in the church of Sant' Agnese fuori le mura on the Via Nomentana in Rome.

**Ambrose** (7 December)
Ambrose (Ambrosius) was born in Trier, in about 340 AD, the son of a Roman prefect in Gaul. When Ambrose's father died, the family returned to Rome. There, Ambrose studied Greek, rhetoric and law and he became a lawyer at the court of justice. He was celebrated as a defender in legal cases, and this resulted in his appointment as consul in Milan. When Bishop Auxentius of Milan died there was a conflict about the succession between Catholics and Arians. The young consul was appointed as a possible successor by the warring factions. Ambrose was baptized, and on 7 December 374, he was ordained Bishop with the dispensation of the Emperor. He negotiated on behalf of the Emperor in legal disputes and became a very respected teacher. When necessary, he even had the courage to take up a position against the state or the Emperor. One of his pronouncements illustrates this: "The Emperor stands in the Church but not above it."

**Antony** (17 January)
Antony came from Central Egypt, where he was born in the town of Keman in about the year 251 AD. His parents were wealthy,

respected citizens. He was attracted by the desert at an early age. Devout hermits lived there in solitary isolation, fleeing from Roman persecution and living in caves in the rocks. One day, he heard the story of the Gospels from a rich young man. Then he sold his considerable inheritance and gave it to the poor. He joined the monks on the edge of the Libyan desert and for twenty years he led an austere and ascetic life, learning to conquer all the temptations of desire and arrogance. More and more monks joined him there. In Alexandria, he defied the Roman persecutors by preaching in public and accusing the Emperors of tyranny. Later he joined a caravan and went to the Red Sea. On Mount Kolzin he found a sheltered spot where he settled and attracted many followers. Antony stayed there up to his death at the age of 105.

### Barlaam and Josaphat (27 November)

Only a legend remains about Barlaam and Josaphat. The story may have been adapted from the Buddha legend, which relates how Prince Gautama grew up in the enclosed environment of the court. When he discovered that there were also such things as sickness, old age and death, he left the court, relinquished all his riches and set out to find a teacher. In the legend of Barlaam and Josaphat the latter was the son of a king and Barlaam was the hermit who became his teacher. In the *Legenda Aurea*, Barlaam and Josaphat are added as saints.

### Beatrice

Nothing more is know about Beatrice apart from the legend related here (published in *Beatrijs, een middeleeuwse* Marialegende in Nijmegen 1951).

### Benedict (21 March)

Benedict literally means "the blessed." He was born in about 480 AD in Nursia in the Sabine mountains. His parents were members of the Roman nobility and sent him to Rome to study law. Benedict fled from the city soon afterwards. He loathed the bustle and the depraved lifestyle which he encountered there and sought solitude in the mountains. The monk Romanus welcomed him in his hut and they lived in isolation for three years. Passing shepherds thought that Benedict, wearing a strange-looking fleece, was a wild animal. A priest who visited him at Eastertide restored the sense of time which he had lost. Then he became a more public figure and was a spiritual guide who gave advice to anyone who came to him. He became the abbot of the Vicovaro monastery. The *Rule of St Benedict* was his own summary of the community rules which formed the basis of a monastic life. Subsequently this Benedictine order spread to many countries and became a great cultural factor throughout Europe.

## Boniface (5 June)

Boniface (Winfrith) was born in the Anglo-Saxon region of Wessex in 672 or 673 AD. He received his first education in the abbey school of Exeter. His father then reluctantly allowed him to enter the Benedictine monastery of Nursling. When he was thirty, he became a priest and travelled to the mainland to convert the Germanic tribes to Christianity. His mission met the greatest opposition in Friesland. Their proud leader, Radboud, continued to perform heathen services and saw the Saxons and Franks as enemies. In Rome, Winfrith visited Pope Gregory II and was given his new name "Boniface," the performer of good deeds. He travelled for many years preaching in Hessen, Thüringen and parts of the Frankish Empire and eventually the Pope made him a bishop. He received a document from Karel Martell which gave him protection at the court of foreign rulers. When he was eighty years old, Boniface returned to Friesland and in the end he gave his own life for the conversion of the Friesians. He was murdered in Dokkum on Whit Sunday in the year 754 AD, together with 52 other Christians.

## Brendan (16 May)

Brendan, one of the greatest Irish saints, was a sailor. According to the legend, he crossed the ocean in a simple sailing boat. He was born in Kerry on the coast of the Dingle peninsula in the extreme west of Ireland. There are still vestiges of his retreat for prayer on the rocky island of Inishtooskert, further north. His birth was accompanied by singular signs. A druid saw the birth of a great king, and that same night thirty cows gave birth to thirty calves very close to his birthplace. The Irish bishop Eric monitored Brendan's education and took him to Limerick, where the nun Ita looked after him as a foster mother. After years of study he became a monk, and travelled to the monasteries of Ireland, Scotland and the many islands where monks had settled. He also travelled far beyond Ireland. He died in the year 578 AD at the age of ninety-three.

## Brigid of Ireland (1 February)

Brigid's father, Dubthach, was a nobleman. When he made one of his young slaves pregnant, the Druids predicted that this slave girl would give birth to a daughter who would surpass every other child in Ireland. The girl was called Brigid (Bride) after one of the most important goddesses in the pantheon of Nordic mythology, who was sometimes known as Dana. In later life, Brigid founded a convent in Kildare where the goddess Dana had been worshipped in ancient times. Brigid was later known as the "Virgin of the Lord of the Elements" which reveals her special relationship with Christ There are many legends about her miracles, and good deeds. She died on 1 February 524 AD, and this day is still celebrated in Ireland, Scotland and the Hebrides.

## Christopher (25 July)

The only fact known about Christopher is that he came from Asia Minor, according to the legend, from the tribe of Canaanites. He lived at the beginning of the third century under the Emperor Decius. Before he was baptized, his name was Reprobus, the damned. His life was a search with the aim of serving the most important and mightiest one on earth. According to the legend, he carried the infant Jesus across a turbulent river on his shoulders. He died a martyr in about 250 AD. St Christopher with the infant Jesus was a favourite subject for artists throughout the centuries. Traditionally, it was believed that seeing his image every day ensured a long and healthy life. This saint has always been honoured as the patron saint of travellers.

## Columba (9 June)

Columba was born in 521 AD in the Irish county of Tyrconnel, from noble parents. In the monastery of the bishop St Finian, he studied the Holy Scriptures and submitted to the strict monastic rules. In 564 AD he was ordained as a priest. A band of disciples wished to follow him. He founded monasteries in both Ireland and Scotland, and introduced rules for the order which were drawn up on the basis of examples of the earliest Christian communities in Asia Minor. The king of the Picts gave Columba the island of Iona. Columba had a large monastery built there and later Irish Christianity spread from there to Europe.

## Cuthbert (20 March)

Cuthbert was born in Northumbria around 634 AD and became a monk at Melrose early in his life. He undertook many missionary journeys and was renowned as a scholar and speaker. He argued for the Roman customs of the Church to be adopted, rather than the Celtic practices, at the famous Synod of Whitby in in 663. Retiring then to Lindisfarne, an island monastery off the north coast of England, he was Prior for a time and then lived as a hermit. He was known for his love of the sea-birds and creatures which surrounded him on his island retreat. He died in 687 and his body remained incorrupt after his death. His relics are now in Durham Cathedral.

## Dionysius the Areopagite

Areopagus was the part of Athens where the temple of Ares (Mars) was located. As a follower of the apostle Paul, Dionysius founded a Christian school in Athens.

Very little is known about Dionysius, and more problems were created in the ninth century or so when the missionary Dionysius (Denis), the first bishop of Paris who is thought to have died around the year 250, came to be confused with the Athenian Dionysius. Further confusion ruled when a third Dionysius, a philosopher of the fifth century, to whom we owe the lively description of the nine heavenly hierarchies of angels, also became confused with the other two.

Many churches were dedicated in France to St Denis who was credited with bringing Christianity to Gaul, sent by Pope Clement. Denis became the patron saint of France and it is his feast-day that we celebrate on 9 October.

## Elizabeth of Hungary (17 November)

Elizabeth was born in 1207, the daughter of the king of Hungary, Andreas II, and his wife Gertrude. Seven years later, the count of Thüringen had a son, Ludwig. Andreas promised that this son could have Elizabeth as a wife. She was sent to the court of Thüringen at the age of four, and she married Ludwig when she was fourteen. She was already living a life of prayer, study, and charitable deeds. She chose the priest, Conrad of Marburg, to be her spiritual leader. She lived an extremely austere life, often she ate only bread and honey, and she wore very simple clothes. She visited the poor and the sick every day and gave away all her wealth. During the famine of 1225, she virtually emptied the treasury so that everyone could have something to eat. Ludwig died on the way to the Crusades, where Conrad of Marburg had sent him. He left Elizabeth and four children at the court where everyone was increasingly hostile to her. She died on 17 November 1231 after building a hospital in Marburg with the remainder of her inheritance.

## Emma

Emma of Haarlem does not belong to the regular canon of saints, and so cannot be found in the Church's calendar of saints. She is a "folk saint" whose behaviour people regarded as "saintly." The medieval legend of Emma of Haarlem, part of the oral tradition of North Holland, was recorded in the middle of the sixteenth century.

## Eustace (20 September)

There are legends about Eustace which tell that he was an important commander called Placidus in the army of the Roman Emperor Trajan in the second century. While he was hunting, he encountered a stag with a luminous Cross between its antlers. After this experience, he was baptized. He was soon subjected to a life of trial and misfortune (like Job in the Old Testament). For fifteen years Eustace bore his heavy burden until he was close to despair. Then his prayers were heard. Under his leadership, the army won a decisive battle and he found the wife and sons he thought he had lost. When the victory was celebrated in Rome he refused to make sacrifices to the ancient gods. The Emperor had him thrown to the lions with his family and other Christians. When the beasts refused to attack them, they were burnt to death.

## Francis of Assisi (4 October)

Francis was born in Assisi in the Italian region of Umbria in 1191. His father was a rich merchant in fabrics. In his youth, Francis led a profligate life. Later he chose a life of poverty, following Christ's words, "Give all your possessions to the poor and follow me." He often went into retreat for long periods and lived a life of solitude in the rugged countryside. There are legends which tell how he spoke to the birds and animals. He founded an order which devoted itself to caring for the poor and the sick. In the "Canticle of the Sun," one of his works which has survived, he praised the perfection of Creation, and of life and death, like a true minstrel.

## Francis of Paola (2 April)

Francis came from Paola, a town in Calabria in Italy. His parents were poor and for a long time they were childless, until their prayers were heard and a son was born to them in about 1416. When he was baptized he was given the name of his patron saint from Assisi. When he was thirteen, his father took him to the Franciscan monastery of San Marco. A year later, he went with his parents on a pilgrimage to Assisi and Rome. When he returned to Paola, he found a cave over the sea to live in and there he prayed and fasted. More and more people went to visit this devout hermit. Fifteen years later, a monastery and a chapel were built there. He called his monks Minims or "minor brothers" and imposed strict rules such as a prohibition on eating meat, dairy products and eggs. Pope Sixtus IV confirmed the new order in 1474. Francis died in Plessis les Tours on 2 April 1507.

## Gall (16 October)

Gall was the name which the Gauls gave to the Irish monk Caillech, who lived in the seventh century. His name is linked with the famous Benedictine monastery in Sankt Gallen on Lake Constance. He crossed to the European mainland from Ireland, to bring the Gospels to the heathens. Columbanus led this mission to the Franks and Germanic tribes. Gall was one of the twelve monks who were under Columbanus's leadership. On some occasions his hot-headedness resulted in the destruction of heathen holy places, which led to hostility amongst the Germanic tribes. When Columbanus ordered him to travel to Northern Italy, he stayed behind at Lake Constance to live there as a hermit. The Sankt Gallen monastery was later built in the place where he spent his final years, and this became a powerful centre of Christian culture, art and science.

## Giles (1 September)

Giles, whose name in Latin is Aegidius — the name means shield-bearer — lived in the eighth century. It is said that he was the son of a king, born in Athens. He became a hermit, and lived in isolated spots to find Christ in himself and in nature. He lived on herbs and roots from the woods. His travels took him to the kingdom of the Franks, first in the Rhone delta, later by the river Gard, and finally to the forests round the city of Nimes. There are legends about his encounters with kings and princes, about his gift for curing the sick and about other miracles that he performed. He is often depicted with the hind which fed him with her milk. He founded the monastery round which the city of St Giles was built. The relics of Giles can be found in the Eglise St Sernin in Toulouse.

**Gregory the Great** (3 September)
During the second half of the sixth century, the city of Rome suffered a period of war, plague, floods and famine. When Pope Pelagius II himself died in an epidemic in 590 AD, the Romans felt that they were totally lost. The people unanimously called on the deacon Gregory to become pope. Gregory was from a wealthy patrician family and initially decided on a political career. He became the prefect of Rome. Later, he retreated to live a life of poverty as a monk. Pope Pelagius II ordained him as deacon and sent him to Constantinople. Gregory was very able at finding solutions for complicated political problems. Before becoming Pope in Rome, he called upon the people to make a pilgrimage. During this trip it is said that Michael appeared on the Mausoleum of the Emperor Hadrian. Ever since then it has been known as the "Castel Sant Angelo." While he was pope, Rome was freed from its troubles. Gregory was able to prevent an imminent war with the Langobards by paying a high ransom. He became best known for the introduction of a new sung liturgy, the Gregorian chant. He died on 12 March 604 AD, and the honorific title on his headstone reads, *Consul Dei,* "Consul of God."

**Jerome** (30 September)
Jerome was born in the Dalmatian city of Stridon, in 347 AD and grew up in a devout and prosperous family. His parents sent him to Rome where he studied grammar, rhetoric and philosophy. From an early age, he was eager to learn, and he soon collected a valuable collection of documents. He was baptized in Rome but still enjoyed a worldly lifestyle. On his first trip to Trier, he decided to devote himself henceforth to Christ. Other journeys took him back to the country of his birth, to Constantinople, where he studied under Gregory, and to Syria and Palestine. For three years he worked in Rome on translations of the Bible, commissioned by Pope Damasus I. For a time Jerome lived as a hermit in the desert of Syria. However, his true vocation was in the field of languages and science. He spent the last thirty-four years of his life in Bethlehem, the place where Jesus was born. Jerome left a wonderful body of work including a translation of the Old Testament from Hebrew.

## John the Evangelist (27 December)

John was one of the twelve Apostles and one of the four evangelists who described the life of Christ. He is also known as John the Divine. His father Zebedee was a fisherman on the lake of Genezareth. With his brother James, he heard John the Baptist, who said of Jesus, "See the Lamb of God who takes away the sins of the world." The two brothers became Jesus's disciples. It is said of John that "the Lord loved him." With Peter and James, he witnessed the appearance of Jesus in a heavenly form, on Mount Tabor. At the Cross, he heard Jesus's words, "See, your mother."

The Gospel written by John differs markedly from the others. Of all the Gospels it is the least based on historical events. It begins with the famous words, "In the beginning was the Word ..."

He was exiled to the island of Patmos, where he foresaw the future of the world and wrote his Book of Revelation, known as *The Apocalypse*. John is depicted with the eagle, the symbol of greatest wisdom.

## George (23 April)

George lived in the third century. His parents were followers of Christ. After his father's death, his mother took him to her birthplace in Palestine. There, George entered the service of the Roman army and managed to reach the rank of tribune. The Emperor Diocletian gave him medals for his noble and courageous character. When the Emperor declared war on Christians, George rejected his medals and went to the Emperor to complain about the bloody battles against the Christians. Diocletian had him imprisoned and tortured. The following day, he was carried through the city and beheaded. The legend of St George and the Dragon is an allegory of his battle against evil.

## Lioba (28 September)

Lioba was born into a noble English family in the south of England in about the year 710 AD. Her mother gave her the name, Truthgeba (God's gift), but she was known as Lioba (beloved). She was educated in the Benedictine abbey of Wimborne in Dorset, where she took her vows. She was related to Boniface, who summoned her to Germany and appointed her as the abbess of the famous convent of Tauberbischofsheim. From there, she also looked after many other convents in the German Empire with wise and loving dedication. St Boniface called her, "the consolation of his life as a pilgrim." When she was very old, she retreated to the royal estate of Schornsheim, near Mainz where she died on 28 September 782 AD, though according to another source, in 779 AD.

**Mary** (born 8 September)
Among all the saints, only in the case of Mary and John the Baptist do we celebrate the day of their birth. It is assumed that Mary was born on the site of the St Anna Church in Jerusalem. For centuries, artists have been inspired by the Annunciation of Jesus's birth to Mary, by the Angel Gabriel. The image of the Virgin bearing a child already existed in pre-Christian mystic schools. The mystery was enshrined by the Roman Catholic Church in the dogma of the "Immaculate Conception," but also refers to the Apocalypse of John the Evangelist. The historical mother of Jesus took the place of pre-Christian goddesses who ruled over fertility and birth. No other saint has been worshipped as much as Mary. Places where she has appeared to people have become centres of pilgrimage, and pilgrims still go to Fatima and Lourdes to seek her presence and ask to be cured.

**Margaret of Antioch** (20 July)
The name Margaret means pearl. She was born in Antioch at the end of the third century, the daughter of a heathen priest. Her wet-nurse told her about the teachings of Christ. Her father exiled her from the land when she told him she wanted to be a Christian. In another country, Margaret became a shepherdess. The Prefect Olybrius saw her in the fields and greatly desired her to be his wife.

When it appeared that she believed in Christ, he had her imprisoned and tortured. Again and again, she miraculously survived this torture, but finally she was put to death by the sword, together with other Christians. According to the legend, she fought against a dragon while she was imprisoned. Her relics are now in Montefiascone near Bolsena, north of Rome.

**Nicholas of Myra** (6 December)
The town of Myra is in Lycia, in south-east Turkey. The apostle Paul brought the gospel to this area, where Nicholas grew up in a devout and prosperous family. There are legends about him giving away his wealth and performing miracles. He decided to lead a monastic life and became an abbot and then the archbishop of Myra. After his death, in 342 AD, the saint was buried in the cathedral of Myra. In 1087, merchants from Bari near Naples, plundered the grave. The

relics of St Nicholas were shipped to Italy and placed in the church of St Stephen in Bari.

## Paschal Baylon (17 May)

Paschal was born on Whit Sunday *(Pascuas de Pentacosta),* 16 May 1540, in a village near Madrid. His parents were simple people who lived off the produce of the land. The boy was often found in church. He liked to herd his sheep near a chapel of St Mary. He taught himself to read in the fields and had dialogues with God. Conscious of the smallest mistakes he made, he asked for forgiveness in the confessional and imposed many restrictions on himself as penance. Later, he wished to remain a lay brother in the Franciscan monastery, was utterly devoted to his work and lived strictly in accordance with the rules of the order. He died on Whit Sunday in 1592. His relics are in the abbey church of Villareal near Valencia.

## Patrick (17 March)

Patrick (Patricius) thought of himself as both a Briton and a Roman. He was born in Scotland between Dunbriton and Glasgow, to a wealthy family. When he was sixteen, robbers took him to Ireland where he was a slave and had to herd the cattle. He bore his fate patiently, and from that time he had visions in which he was called upon to be an apostle for Ireland. He became a priest and a bishop, spread the Gospels, baptized and preached, and founded monasteries and churches. There are many legends about the miracles he performed and the kings and druids he converted. After his death, Ireland became a great centre of Christian culture.

## Radegund (13 August)

Radegund was born in about 518 AD, the daughter of the king of Thüringen, Berthachar. During her youth, she was surrounded by intrigue and murder. Her father, mother and sisters all met a violent death. When Thüringen was invaded by the Franks, they took the royal children with them as hostages. Thus when she was thirteen years old, Radegund was taken to Athies near Soissons where she was baptized and brought up as a Christian. She was predestined to marry Chlotar, the king of the Franks. After failing to escape from this marriage, she accepted her fate. Once she was Queen, she tried to withdraw as much as possible from the life of luxury at court and sought to live a life of solitude, prayer and penance. She used her powerful position to ask for prisoners to be pardoned and to work for the construction of a hospital for the poor. She spent her own income entirely on charity. In the hospital she looked after the sick with her own hands. Radegund fled the court when Chlotar had her younger brother murdered. After many prayers, she took the veil and devoted herself to a monastic life.

### Thomas (21 December)

Thomas was one of Jesus's disciples. He was "the unbeliever" who would not believe in the Resurrection until he had placed his finger in Jesus's wounds. There are legends about his travels to the east, as far as India, where he spread the Gospels. At the time, King Gundaphar ruled the Indian Empire. It is said that he was also converted by Thomas.

The Gospel of St Thomas, which he allegedly wrote, contains legends and stories which appear to have a Buddhist element. There is a rock in Mailapur near Madras in southern India where it is said that Thomas died by the sword in about 67 AD. The relics were solemnly transferred to Edessa, in what is now Iraq, in the year 232 AD, and later to the Greek island of Chios. Finally, they were bought to Ortona on the Adriatic coast near Naples.

### Veronica (4 February/12 July)

There is a legend about Veronica as one of Jesus's pupils. She is said to have wiped the sweat and blood off his face on the Way of the Cross. The cloth became the subject of many stories about miraculous cures, and later it was considered a valuable relic.

In recent times, the day of Veronica has been celebrated on 12 July. This was in remembrance of Veronica Giuliano who lived from 1660 to 1716. This Capuchin nun from Umbria had the signs of the stigmata, the wounds of the crucified Lord, and she was canonized in 1839.

Selma Lagerlöf tells the story more fully in her *Christ Legends*.

# Index of Pictures

# Index of Saints

## BY NAME

## BY DATE

January 17: Antony
January 21: Agnes
February 1: Brigid
February 4: Veronica
March 17: Patrick
March 20: Cuthbert
March 21: Benedict
April 2: Francis of Paola
April 23: George
May 16: Brendan
May 17: Paschal
May 30: Joan of Arc
June 5: Boniface
June 9: Columba
July 20: Margaret
July 25: Christopher
August 13: Radegund
September 1: Giles
September 3: Gregory

September 8: Mary
September 20: Eustace
September 28: Lioba
September 30: Jerome
October 4: Francis of Assisi
October 9: Dionysius (Denis)
October 16: Gall
October 18: Luke
October 28: Jude
November 11: Martin
November 17: Elizabeth
November 27: Barlaam and
    Josaphat
December 6: Nicholas
December 7: Ambrose
December 13: Odilia
December 21: Thomas
December 21: John

# PATRON SAINTS

Agnes: Girls; betrothed couples; gardeners
Ambrose: Bee-keepers
Antony of Egypt: Basket-makers; hermits
Benedict: Monks; school-children; Europe
Boniface: Brewers; tailors
Brendan: Seafarers
Brigid: Dairymaids; midwives; poets
Christopher: Travellers, motorists
Columba: Poets
Cuthbert: Shepherds
Dionysius (Denis): France
Elizabeth of Hungary: Charities; bakers
Eustace: Huntsmen
Francis of Assisi: Animals and birds; ecology
Francis of Paola: Sailors

Gall: Birds
George: Soldiers; England
Giles: The lame; horses
Gregory the Great: Singers; masons
Jerome: Librarians
Joan of Arc: Soldiers; France
John the Evangelist: Writers; publishers
Jude: Hopeless causes
Luke the Evangelist: Artists; doctors
Margaret of Antioch: Women; nurses
Martin: Beggars
Mary: Nuns; virgins
Nicholas of Myra: Children; pawnbrokers; Russia
Odilia: The blind; Alsace
Patrick: Ireland
Thomas: Builders; architects
Veronica: Washerwomen

## THE LEGENDS AT FESTIVALS AND SEASONS

*Advent*
Mary expecting the Messiah
Nicholas in the storm, salvation from danger
Boniface building a place to worship
Lioba keeping a place to worship

*Christmas*
Brigid/Bride birth of the child

*Epiphany*
Cuthbert the true bread
Dionysius the Areopagite wisdom of the stars, wisdom of the earth
Benedict wisdom in the world

*February*
Jude the image of Christ
Veronica the image which heals
Luke the image of Mary

*Lent*
Patrick passage through Hell
Gall the obedient bear
Elizabeth being a stranger
Beatrice prodigal son
Radegund miracle of the oats
Emma of Haarlem the woman who carries the man

*Easter*
Antony appearance of Christ
Thomas building in heaven
Paschal water from the earth
Willibrord and Egbert water from the earth
John the Evangelist invulnerability
Barlaam and Josaphat the new country

*Ascension*
Ambrose celestial bread

*Whitsun*
Gregory light from above
Odilia gaining sight
Agnes the heavenly bridegroom
Boniface the new language

*St John's Day*
Christopher bearing Christ
Columba guilt and penance

*Summer*
Brendan journey across the (inner) sea
Lioba conquering fire
Jerome using the strength of a lion

*St Michael's Day*
George fighting the dragon
Margaret fighting the dragon
Joan of Arc serving Michael

*November*
Martin dark times
Eustace dark times
Giles dark times

*General*
Francis love of nature, animals, birds